EVERYDAY THINGS AND THEIR STORY

THE ROMANTIC STORY
OF MODERN INDUSTRY
AND HOW IT SUPPLIES
OUR DAILY NEEDS

ODHAMS PRESS LTD., LONG ACRE, LONDON, W.C.2

CONTENTS

CUP-MAKING UNIT—EARLY STAGES

In the background the cup is being shaped from a ball of clay by the jolley. In the foreground it is shown, still in the original porous state, as a finished cup, the handle being attached on the way. After this process it is ready for the first firing.

CHINA AND POTTERY

Classification. Earthenware, Stoneware and Porcelain. Materials. The Pug Mill. Throwing. The Potter's Wheel. Biscuit Firing. The Jolley. Lathe Finishing. Glazing. Glost Kiln. Hand-Painting. Hazards of Firing.

POTTERY enters into our lives in far more ways than by providing us with cups and saucers, basins and jugs. The sanitation of towns and cities depends on millions of stoneware drain-pipes hidden below pavements and roads. The potter is responsible for the fittings of kitchen and bath-room, for the glazed materials, with their property of resisting atmospheric corrosion, that face many buildings, and for much of the brightness of the modern home.

The earliest pottery was vessels for food and drink; and how man first came to shape clay into such vessels is largely a matter of guess-work. Primitive men made baskets from wicker and osiers and lined these with clay to make them water-tight. It is supposed that perhaps one of these baskets fell into the fire on which a meal was being cooked, so causing the wicker to burn whilst leaving the clay lining intact and hard. This theory is partly based on the fact that the markings on some of the ancient vessels resemble basket-work. Later on, perhaps, some enterprising forerunners of the modern potter learned how to build up vessels from coils of clay without any wicker shape as a guide, baking them in an oven or kiln. On the other hand, in tropical countries shapes were copied from coconuts, gourds and other natural objects, the ware not being baked but simply dried in the sun. This remains to-day the practice in certain eastern countries, where it is particularly noticeable also in the making of bricks.

In the widest sense of the word, pottery includes ware of any kind that is made from clay and hardened by intense heat. Ceramics, the name given

KNEADING IN THE PUG MILL

Fig. 1. *Clay being removed from the pug mill, where it is kneaded into a homogeneous mass. It is now ready to be cut into suitable lengths for the potter.*

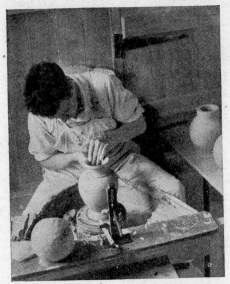

THROWING BY ELECTRICITY

Fig. 2. *As the clay revolves on an electrically turned wheel, the thrower moulds it deftly into the required shape with his fingers.*

rock that has been disintegrated and changed during countless centuries by erosion and climatic conditions. Almost every district in the world possesses some form of clay suitable for pottery-making, but England is particularly lucky in the quality of her native clays.

The commoner clays, which are impregnated with metallic ores and other foreign substances, are useful only in the manufacture of such articles as bricks and tiles. The purest form of clay, known as kaolin or China clay, was first introduced into England in the 18th century, being found in China, France and Germany. There was no suspicion that it existed in England until 1755, when William Cookworthy discovered deposits in Cornwall. This clay is composed of hydrated silicate of alumina, mixed with smaller proportions of lime, soda and potash, and is derived from

to the art of pottery as a whole, is derived from a Greek word meaning "pottery". Ceramics may be broadly divided into the three important groups —earthenware, stoneware, and porcelain. Each of these groups may be sub-divided, leaving certain wares—such as English bone china, terra-cotta and fireclay—that are difficult to classify.

Earthenware is composed of material that is exposed only to a moderate heat in the process of baking—say, from 850° to 1,200° C.—and the finished article can be scratched by any pointed instrument. Stoneware is baked at a great heat, and results in a harder substance. Porcelain is fired at the highest possible temperature, probably about 1,450° C., and includes the more delicate examples of the potter's craft.

The difference between the materials used in the three groups is one of composition. The most important material is, of course, clay—originally stone and

THE FILTER PRESS

Fig. 3. *Liquid clay is pumped under pressure into cloth bags and forms flat cakes or slabs ready for the pug mill.*

THE CUP JOLLEY

Fig. 4. *The ball of clay is put in a plaster mould and worked roughly into shape. The inside is shaped by a metal profile inserted into the cup while it is still in the mould.*

decomposed granite rock. Large deposits of another very important clay, known as "ball" clay, have been found to exist in Dorset.

No two clay-pits in the world furnish an identical clay—even the clay from the same pit varies in composition. This extraordinary circumstance renders constant laboratory tests necessary to ensure uniform results.

Other ingredients used in the various pottery products are Cornish stone, calcined flint, and calcined bone. The use of the last-mentioned material gives English china its unique semi-translucent, ivory-like quality, from which it derives its name of English bone-china.

The visitor to a modern pottery is usually surprised by the number of processes involved in the actual preparation of the clay before it is sent to the potter. When it comes in from the pits the clay has already been matured to a certain extent by exposure, but it is necessary for it to undergo a further period of maturing in the clay cellars. It then passes through a series of gigantic grinding mills and mixers, in which various other ingredients are added. All the ingredients are thoroughly mixed with water, forming a thick liquid of about the consistency of cream. This liquid, known as "slip", remains for some time in large vessels, called "arks", and is then passed on to the sifter. Here the dirt is removed, and an electromagnet extracts the particles of iron that would cause brown flecks and stains to appear in the finished ware.

The pure slip is now forced by a pressure pump into a long clay press, which consists of a series of sailcloth covers screwed up in flat metal frames (Fig. 3). Most of the water is squeezed out of the clay by the screw pressure, and the press cloths are removed. The flat layers of the now plastic clay are rolled up and thrown into a "pug mill", where a series of rapidly-revolving blades, operating as a kind of mincing machine, transform the rolls of clay into a solid plastic mass, free from the air pockets that would cause blisters to arise during the firing. The clay is slowly forced out of the mill through a tubular mouth and the resulting rolls are cut into convenient lengths for use by the potters (Fig. 1).

If the ware is being made by the casting process the clay remains as slip, in which state it is poured into a dry plaster mould. A thin

APPLYING THE HANDLES

Fig. 5. *Handles are put on to the cups by hand with the aid of a little liquid clay. This operation is a very delicate one, as the clay is still in a soft, pliable state.*

GLAZING

Fig. 6. *After firing the pottery is dipped into liquid glaze, which it absorbs, leaving a film of glaze on the surface. Further firing will give the glaze a shiny surface.*

layer of clay adheres to the sides of the mould, and when the correct thickness is attained the superfluous slip is poured off. The various parts of the mould are then removed, leaving the required shape ready for further processes.

The most fascinating of all the processes in pottery-making—and one which has changed but little since biblical times—is known as "throwing". It is so called from the fact that the ball of clay from which the shape is to be formed is first thrown by the potter on to the centre of a revolving wheel.

One of the far-reaching discoveries in pottery-making was the use of the "wheel", for it makes possible the building up of symmetrical shapes with a considerable degree of accuracy. The age of the potter's wheel is not known,

but it was certainly used by the Persians, Egyptians, and other peoples of long ago. It is mentioned in the Bible and is also referred to by Homer. Actual drawings of potters forming vases and other shapes on the wheel have been found in Egyptian tombs, and some authorities think it was invented in Egypt.

At first the wheel was probably turned with one hand and the ware shaped with the other, but later a wheel was evolved that could be worked by the foot. There was little essential change in the design of the wheel until about the middle of last century, when Henry Doulton of Lambeth applied steam power to drive the wheel, thus leaving the craftsman free to concentrate his attention on the work of his hands. To-day, electrically-driven wheels are generally used (Fig. 2).

E.T.T.S.—A*

After the ball of clay has been centred on the revolving wheel it is gradually drawn up and pressed down again several times to perfect its texture. Finally, it is opened out by the skilful manipulation of the potter's thumbs and fingers. By clasping the clay with both hands and exerting the required pressure, the potter brings the clay to the required height, and at length the final shape of the article begins to emerge, from what but a little while before was a mere shapeless lump of clay.

CUP-MAKING BY JOLLEY

For mass production of cups, saucers, plates, and similar articles, "jolleys" and "jiggers" are used. These machines are perhaps best described as mechanical throwing machines. A jolley has a metal head, in which is placed a dry plaster mould; clay is then inserted in this mould, the machine revolving in a similar manner to a potter's wheel. A lever brings down an arm that carries a metal profile of the interior outline of the cup or pot. The arm forces the clay against the wall of the mould, thus forming the inside of the article, whilst the mould itself forms the outside (Fig. 4). Several thousand cups can easily be made on such a machine by two operatives in a normal working day.

After a vase or other object has been "thrown", or shaped, on the wheel, it is left to dry for some time until it is judged ready for finishing on the lathe. This process makes the article perfectly smooth and free from imperfections, also brings it down to certain definite measurements. As may be imagined this is a very important point in the manufacture of such articles as electrical insulators. Sometimes, of course, there is a beauty in the very roughness of a vase—particularly a salt-glazed stoneware vase—and in the case of such articles the finishing process is omitted.

Ware made by mechanical processes is automatically of the correct size, and it is also smooth. In the case of these articles, the finishing process consists only of the removal of any seams that may have arisen at the points where the various parts of the plaster mould are joined together. It is fascinating to watch the turner at work, stripping off the shavings of clay as if he were turning a piece of wood.

At this stage various other processes also take place—for example, handles and spouts are made and fixed on with slip (Fig. 5). The clay may be decorated by carving, by incising, or by applying liquid slip from a special tool when a design in raised outline is required.

If the vase or bowl is made of stoneware it is also glazed and coloured whilst the clay is still unfired, and this is the only remaining process necessary before it is ready to take its place in the showrooms. Only one firing is given to stoneware, but earthenware and china are always fired at least twice. Some delicately coloured figures and richly decorated table services must go through the kilns even three or more times.

SAGGARS

Before being fired the ware is carefully placed in already burnt clay receptacles known as "saggars", another of the expressive names peculiar to pottery-making. Saggars are pans made from a refractory clay that the heat cannot damage. They protect the ware for the eighty hours or more during which it is in the oven.

This first firing is known as the "biscuit" firing, the kilns being known as "biscuit" ovens. The art of stacking the saggars to the best advantage in the kilns calls for considerable experience on the part of the kiln men. When it comes from the ovens the ware is now in the "biscuit" state, and is decorated

FIXING THE GLAZE

Fig. 7. *After glazing, the pottery is fired in the glost kiln to give the glaze a shiny finish. It is seen here going into the electric oven, each piece carefully separated on the trays.*

either by under-glaze ceramic colours by hand, or else by prints taken from engraved copper plates.

A whole book could be written on the subject of glazes alone. In Ancient Egypt and Assyria the glazes were silicates of soda and lime, but these were later superseded by glazes produced from red and white lead, felspar, salt, and other materials.

Though hard, biscuit ware is porous, and absorbs the liquid clay into which it is dipped. The dipper takes the article in his hand and with a single motion plunges it into the dipping tube. Lifting it out, he causes the glaze to run equally over the whole surface by swerves and twists of swift precision (Fig. 6). The glazed article is now placed on a kind of

platform on which shelves rest on swivels. From here it passes into a hot-air chamber from which it descends again, now dry but dull in appearance.

Another ordeal by fire now awaits the ware in the oven, or "glost" kiln, where its coat of glaze is hardened (Fig. 7). It is not such a fierce trial this time, for firing lasts one day. For two days it is cooled, to emerge with a bright, clear, impermeable glaze. It is now ready for any further "on-glaze" decoration that may be required. This application of rich enamel colours—gold, silver and lustres—is done by hand, by copper plate, or by litho transfers (Fig. 8). At the Royal Doulton Pottery at Burslem, a staff of famous artists is engaged in this work of painting and decorating;

DECORATING THE FINISHED CHINA

Fig. 8. *Colours are painted by hand on to the printed outline pattern. A final firing, or even a number of firings, will be required to give a brilliant and lasting finish.*

they create pieces of delightful colouring and exquisite beauty, many of them destined to become the heirlooms of to-morrow.

This decoration may necessitate several journeys to the enamel kiln, where the colours are fixed as the artist's work progresses.

Whatever the actual process of forming the pottery, all ware has to go through the kilns or ovens at least once, and of all the hazards of pottery making the firing is the most severe. No kiln was ever opened that did not contribute its quota of ruined pieces, and no matter what precautions may be taken it is impossible to forecast what the result will be. So much depends upon the position in the kiln in which the ware is placed, and on the amount of oxygen admitted into the kiln at the various stages during the firing process. The generation of heat must be very slow, and the temperature must be increased only gradually, or the glaze will crack or peel and the pots be liable to warp.

Sometimes effects are obtained in firing that exceed anything that even the potter himself had foreseen; this applies in particular to the effects achieved by the mingling of the various glazes. Coal-fired kilns are still used for stoneware. Gas and electrically-fired kilns are now used generally for the manufacture of fine types of pottery, earthenware, china, and porcelain.

GLASS AND GLASSWARE

What Glass is made of. Furnace and Lehr. Crown Glass. Table Glassware.
Bottles. Making Sheet Glass. Libbey-Owens and Bicheroux Processes. Modern
Methods. Polishing. Safety Glass. Glass Bricks and Glass Houses.

MILLIONS of people—wherever they go, wherever they live—see most of the world through glass: through spectacles, through windows. A world without windows—we can hardly imagine it. Many of us have vivid memories of glass—scattered over streets on the morning after an air-raid; glass piled along the curbs in road after road—forcible reminders of our dependence upon this strange substance.

For strange substance it undoubtedly is; unlike the vast majority of solid substances, glass is non-crystalline in structure—what the physicist calls "amorphous", indeed, one of the glassmaker's tasks is to prevent the formation of crystals during manufacture.

Glass is made of silica—one atom of the element silicon combined with two of oxygen—fused at great heat with the help of a flux of some kind such as soda. This mixture has not a fixed melting point; it does not change suddenly from solid to liquid. When red-hot it is a soft, very tenacious, solid, malleable like putty and easily cut with knives or scissors. As it heats it changes to a thick syrup and then to a thin watery fluid.

As this fluid cools the inner and outer molecules do not cohere into a solid state simultaneously; the outer parts of the mass solidify before the inner parts and the glass, therefore, is full of internal strains. That is why glass is always more or less brittle. If the mass cools too suddenly, some of the molecules may rearrange themselves as crystals of silica or of soda, and it is this possibility that troubles the glassmaker. For it is in the nature of crystals to increase in size, and ever-growing crystals in a body of glass set up strains and stresses which, sooner or later, must inevitably shatter it.

Silica melted with soda makes a kind of glass. But it is not quite the right sort of glass for bottles or windows, because it melts in water. This silicate of soda is the soluble glass—waterglass—used for preserving eggs. For glass as we know it in general use, the silicate of soda or potash must be combined with silicates of an alkaline earth or metal. Many different kinds can be formed by carefully varying the combinations of silicates used. The chief groups are window glass and plate glass (also called crown glass), which are made from silicate of soda and lime; flint glass (table ware, "crystal glass"), made from

THE FIRST STEP

Fig. 1. *The crucibles or "pots" used for melting the ingredients of the best glass, which is still made by hand.*

GENERAL ARRANGEMENTS OF A MODERN

Fig. 2. *Type of melting furnace commonly employed. Raw material is introduced*

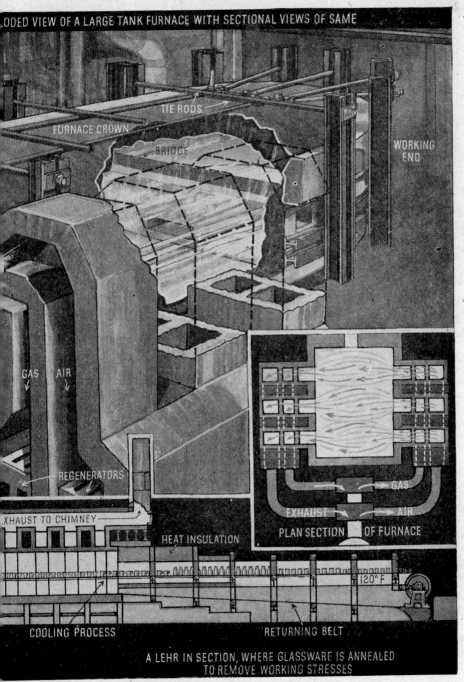

ODED VIEW OF A LARGE TANK FURNACE WITH SECTIONAL VIEWS OF SAME

TIE RODS

FURNACE CROWN

BRIDGE

WORKING END

GAS AIR

REGENERATORS

GAS

EXHAUST TO CHIMNEY

EXHAUST AIR

PLAN SECTION OF FURNACE

HEAT INSULATION

120° F

COOLING PROCESS

RETURNING BELT

A LEHR IN SECTION, WHERE GLASSWARE IS ANNEALED
TO REMOVE WORKING STRESSES

GLASS FURNACE FOR MASS PRODUCTION
at the "doghouse" and refined glass drawn out at the opposite end. Below right, the lehr.

A STAGE IN THE BICHEROUX PROCESS

Fig. 3. *This process, introduced in 1921, improved and speeded up the making of plate glass. As the melted glass was passed between two rollers a flatter sheet was produced which needed less grinding and polishing. (Above) a "pot" being removed from the furnace.*

silicate of potash and lead; and bottle glass, made from silicate of lime and alumina, or silicate of potash or soda, iron or manganese.

It will be seen that the glassmaker's raw materials are very common substances—except for potash, which is not so plentiful as we could wish. Fortunately the makers of flint glass have a practical substitute in carbonate of soda, which is easily made from common salt.

Other ingredients affect the product's hardness, brightness, clearness, elasticity, colour and so on. Coloured glass is obtained by introducing various metals. A trace of cobalt gives a rich blue, so does copper; copper with a little gold gives either a deep red or a bright green. Uranium makes a yellow-green and manganese a purple; added nickel oxide produces a violet-tinted glass which keeps out ordinary light but admits the ultra-violet rays which are unable to pass through clear glass.

But it is not putting the colour in, it is keeping it out that bothers the glassmakers. Iron is the great bugbear, for the minutest trace gives the glass a pale green tint. In spite of elaborate cleansing of the raw materials, it is difficult to rid them completely of iron oxide, so decolorising agents—manganese dioxide, arsenic, nickel and others—are often added when perfectly clear and colourless glass is required.

Mechanisation has now invaded the

SPINNING A DISC TO MAKE SHEET GLASS

TIE RODS & BRACING FRAME

WORKING WINDOW

POT

EYE OF FURNACE

FURNACE SIEGE

← COAL DOOR

ROASTING COAL MAKES PRODUCER GAS

EXHAUST GASES ESCAPE BY WAY OF REGENERATOR PASSAGES

AIR ADMISSION

2 TYPES OF MELTING POTS

CROWN

EXHAUST

SIEGE

EYE

HOT AIR

GAS

SECTION OF FURNACE & REGENERATOR

DETAILS OF A REGENERATIVE POT FURNACE FOR GLASS MAKING

A GLASS FURNACE

Fig. 4. *Shown in section, here is the old-fashioned glass furnace as developed according to modern ideas. The glass-blower is making sheet glass by the time honoured method.*

industry, but the general principles are still much the same, so we will look first at the hand methods.

Whatever variety of glass is being made, the ingredients are carefully weighed out and placed in a mechanical mixer. They generally include a large proportion of "cullet"—broken glass put in to make the melting easier. The "batch" is then taken by trucks to the furnace, where the materials are shovelled into the melting pot until it is full. The pot is heated and the contents melt. Under the great heat gases are driven off and the pot's contents decrease in volume. More material is added, again and again, until the pot is at last filled with molten glass (Fig. 1).

The pots, which may hold from about 5 cwt. to 25 cwt., are set on the floor or "siege" of the furnace, the heat rising up from the centre or "eye" and being deflected on to the pots by a roof of refractory material. In the old type of English furnace—many of which are still in use—there may be twelve pots, each 38 inches in diameter and holding about 15 cwt. of metal. Such a furnace is capable of melting about 8 tons of glass per week, using 40 tons of coal. In the modern type of "regenerative" furnace coal-firing has been superseded by producer-gas firing, giving greater economy and efficiency.

In the regenerative tank furnace, hot gases are made to pass backwards and forwards through a complicated system of passages, the direction of the currents being changed by valves and dampers. Underneath the floor of the furnace, or at each side of it, are passages partly filled with open brickwork; these are the regenerators. Hot air is admitted through the brickwork in one of the passages and producer gas through the adjoining passage, air and gas combining with intense heat under the crown of the furnace and passing out through the regenerators opposite.

REGENERATIVE TANK FURNACE

The bricks on the exhaust side become highly heated and, after a time, the currents of air and fuel gas are switched over, the exhaust flues becoming the entry flues and vice versa. Thus the regenerators in turn become heated and give up their heat to the entering gas and air (Fig. 2).

The constituents of glass melt at temperatures between 1,400° C. and 1,500° C., which is about three times that of a brightly glowing coal fire.

At some stage of its manufacture glass must be annealed, or unequal cooling of the glass sets up stresses and tensions within the outer and inner parts. A sudden change of temperature increases these, and the article cracks, or "flies". Annealing gives more equal distribution of the tensions throughout the glass. The

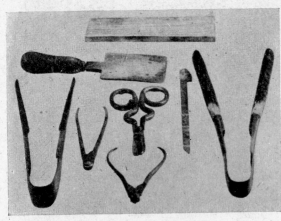

TOOLS OF THE CRAFT

The glassmaker does his work with surprisingly few and very simple tools. A "smoother", a "palette", callipers and scissors (shown above) are all he needs.

GLASS-BLOWERS AT WORK

Fig. 5. *Glass-blowing calls for great skill and sound judgment. Innumerable forms are produced by blowing, swinging or rotating the glass gathered on the end of the pipe.*

finished articles are placed in an annealing furnace or "lehr", immediately they are made. The lehr is a long tunnel heated to a temperature of, perhaps, 470° C. at the front end. The glass is placed in trays, or on conveyor belts and, as it passes through the tunnel, the temperature is decreased.

The speed at which the glass travels through the lehr depends on its thickness and is regulated by a variable-speed electric motor driving the conveyor. Milk bottles, for example, require about 1½ hours, but some articles require 4 or 5 hours or even longer.

To make a sheet of glass by what is known as the old crown glass process, the workman dips the long blowpipe in the molten glass again and again,

until he has gathered on the end of it a bulb-shaped lump. By rolling this on the iron table or "marver", he makes the bulb conical and then, by blowing this, he makes a large hollow pear. The glass has now become too cold and is reheated; then, by alternate blowing and heating, the pear changes to a large sphere with a point on the underside, called the bullion point (Fig. 5).

Next he uses the iron rod, called a "pontil" or "ponty". At one end of this there is a little depression. When the iron has been made hot the bullion point on the flattened sphere of glass is pressed against this depression which becomes firmly attached. The blowpipe is removed from the other end of the sphere with a piece of cold iron, leaving a rim of glass where the pipe has been. The glass now looks rather like an over-blown wine decanter with a short neck.

The workman next carries the sphere, supported on the ponty, to an opening in a furnace and softens the neck where the blowpipe was. He twirls the ponty and the neck becomes wider; the ponty is then set in a rest in front of the furnace and slowly revolved. The over-blown decanter changes to an outsize in goldfish bowls, with a wide lip or rim around the opening. As the glass softens in the heat from the opening in the furnace, the ponty is revolved faster and faster. The spinning mass makes a draught which draws out the flames so that they lick at the glass. With a sudden rush of sound the sides of the bowl open out, forming a flat disk of glass on the revolving ponty (Fig. 4).

Crystal or flint glass, which is made from sand, potash and lead, is brilliant and sparkling. As a rule, table glassware is made by the workman without moulds, but less costly articles may be produced by blowing the bulb of hot glass in a mould, to be finished by hand.

Glassmakers work in groups, or "chairs", of three men and a boy, each having his own task. The "foot-maker" starts the work; the "servitor" makes stems and feet; the "workman" shears the rim and finishes the article; the fourth, the "boy", assists all three.

MAKING A STEMMED GLASS

In making a vase, wine-glass or any article with a stem and a foot, the foot-maker takes his blowing iron—a steel tube 4 or 5 ft. in length and from $\frac{1}{2}$ to $1\frac{1}{4}$ in. in diameter—and "gathers" on it sufficient molten glass to make the bowl. He rolls this backwards and forwards on a polished cast-iron table, or "marver", to round it, then blows down the tube, thus distending the glass into a bulb. By swinging the tube about he now causes the bulb to assume the desired shape (see Figs. 8 and 9).

Having blown the bowl, the footmaker passes the work on to the servitor, who "casts on" to the end of the bowl a blob of molten glass which he pulls out into the form of a stem. At the end of the stem he casts on another blob which he squeezes out to form the foot. The work is then passed to the workman, who touches the article with a piece of cold iron near the blowing tube, when a sharp tap causes it to break off the tube. It is then put into a special holder, known as a gadget, and, as it has now become cool, the workman holds it in the furnace to heat it so as to make it workable again. This done, he cuts the jagged edge with his shears

THE GLASS-BLOWER IN HIS CHAIR

Fig. 6. *Note the long arms with which he imparts a spinning movement to the glass on his pipe.*

and shapes the rim by spinning it up and down wooden arms at each side of his bench—the "chair" (Fig. 6). Jugs are made in a similar manner, except that usually no foot is cast on. These cannot be put on a gadget, so a little molten glass is gathered on the end of the ponty, by which it is thus stuck to the bottom of the jug. The fracture left by the ponty when it is eventually broken from the article is known as the "ponty mark" and is clearly seen in antique glasses; in modern glasses this mark is polished out.

When a jug is being made the lip is fashioned by pressing down the rim when hot. The handle consists of a thick rod of hot glass that has been made by the boy. The workman turns this rod over to meet the top of the jug after it has been stuck on to the middle. Jugs and vases are widened or reduced in form by means of varying pressure applied with a pair of "pucellas", a kind of tongs. The bottoms are flattened by the "battledore" or "palette", a flat wooden board with a handle (Fig. 7).

A TRICKY JOB

Fig. 7. *Making and fixing a semicircular handle to a glass jug by bending a rod of hot glass to shape.*

BLANKS ANNEALED

When these "blanks", as the plain glasses are called, have been made, they are annealed by passing them through a lehr. On being withdrawn they are carefully examined and those with the least flaw are immediately broken. The remainder go to the decorating shop, where the design to be cut is first marked out by girls who copy the master pattern on each blank with special red paint. When this paint is dry the blank goes to the glass-cutter for decoration according to the pattern.

Glass-cutting is done in two stages. First the blank goes to the "rougher", who works with a revolving disk—either of iron or carborundum—with a bevelled edge. A fine stream of water and sand drips on to the wheel and, by these abrasives, the main cuts of the pattern are ground, or "cut". The beauty of the cut depends on the skill of the workman, who holds the glass against the wheel and moves it about according to the pattern to be cut. The article next passes to a "smoother". He works at a frame exactly like that of the rougher, but uses a stone wheel, whose abrasive action is finer than that of the first wheel. The smoother goes over the work of the rougher, adding the fine and intricate cuts. The rough cuts are smoothed out and then polished with polishing powder on wooden and brush wheels.

The glass has now the familiar cut pattern; but all the cuts have a frosted surface which must be polished. The modern way of doing this is by the acid-polishing process, in which girls dip the articles into vats containing a mixture of sulphuric and hydrofluoric acids; by removing a thin film of glass, these acids put a brilliant polish on the piece.

There would be no sense in patiently grinding by hand articles that can be ground by machine—the bottoms of tumblers, for example. These are ground, smoothed and polished on automatic machines at the rate of some 2,000 per day. Each machine has four vertical revolving wheels—one of iron, two of stone and one of wood—against each of which in turn the bottom of the tumbler is pressed. The iron wheel roughs the tumbler, the two stone wheels smooth and the wooden wheel polishes.

So far we have dealt with glass made by the old handicraft methods. But we do not come upon hand-fashioned glassware except as an occasional treat. Cheap glass, mountains of mass-produced glass, is what the world demands.

For example, as millions of bottles of all kinds and sizes are made and used every year in Great Britain, it would be impossible and uneconomical to make them by hand. The work is done by remarkable automatic machines, the

first of which was invented in the United States by M. J. Owens, and introduced into Great Britain in 1912.

An improvement on the Owens automatic machine was made by Redfern. A fifteen-arm automatic machine of the Redfern type is capable of making bottles ranging in height from 2½ to 16 inches with a maximum diameter of 6 inches, and will produce 120 pint bottles per minute, or more than 1,000,000 bottles a week, working twenty-four hours a day.

The Redfern machine consists essentially of fifteen separate bottle-making units, grouped about a central column and, in appearance, resembles the roundabout of a country fair. The central column is stationary, the units revolving around it and close to a "pot" containing a supply of molten glass. Each unit produces a bottle in the course of one revolution round the column; as the machine may be run up to a speed of six revolutions per minute it will be seen that as many as ninety bottles a minute may be produced.

The units are self-contained, each being provided with a blowing head, to the

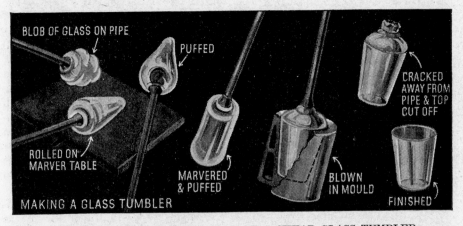

BLOB OF GLASS ON PIPE

PUFFED

CRACKED AWAY FROM PIPE & TOP CUT OFF

ROLLED ON MARVER TABLE

MARVERED & PUFFED

BLOWN IN MOULD

FINISHED

MAKING A GLASS TUMBLER

STAGES IN THE HAND BLOWING OF A CHEAP GLASS TUMBLER

Fig. 8. *Showing how by simple processes a finished tumbler may be made from a blob of glass by rolling, puffing and blowing. Nowadays machine methods are used for mass production.*

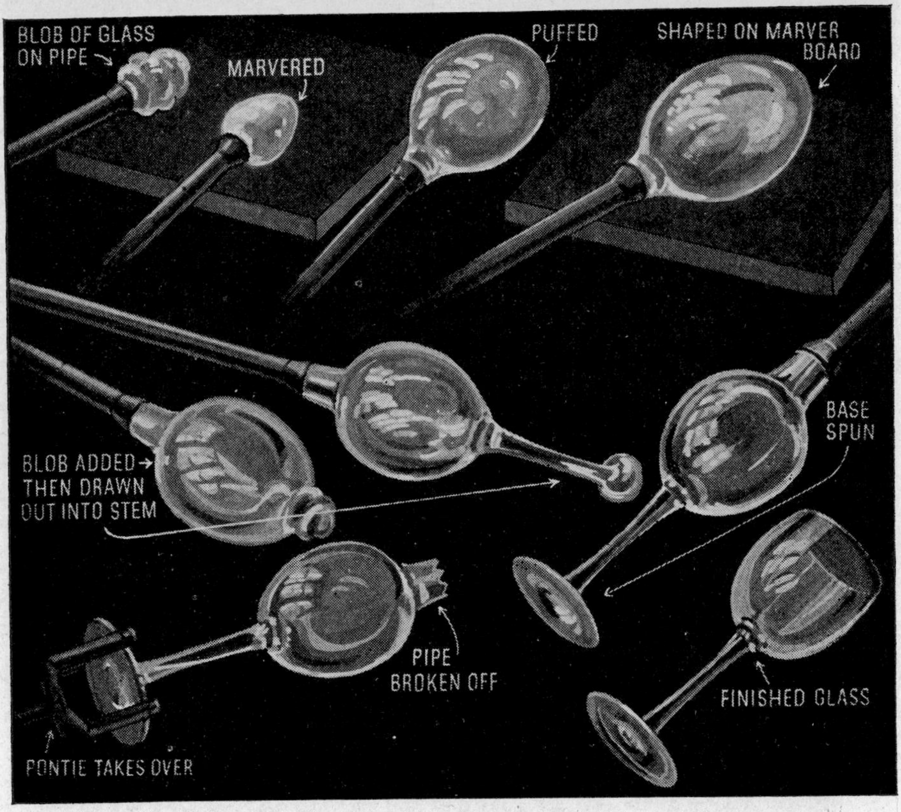
BLOB OF GLASS ON PIPE
MARVERED
PUFFED
SHAPED ON MARVER BOARD
BLOB ADDED THEN DRAWN OUT INTO STEM
BASE SPUN
PIPE BROKEN OFF
FINISHED GLASS
PONTIE TAKES OVER

STAGES IN MAKING A STEMMED GLASS

Fig. 9. *The glass is made in the stages here shown by a unit or "chair" of three men, the footmaker, servitor (who makes stems) and workman (who finishes the article).*

underside of which a split ring mould for forming the neck or top of the bottle is pivoted. Below is the split blank mould in which is made the blank or "parison".

As the blowing head passes over the surface of a revolving pot containing the molten glass, it dips and lowers the bottom of the blank mould into the glass. A powerful vacuum sucks up the white-hot glass into the mould, in the centre of which a plunger has just been lowered. The molten glass glows round the end of the plunger and fills the ring mould, forming the neck of the bottle, with its initial opening or "mouth". The contact between the molten glass and the plunger and ring mould rapidly cools and sets this portion of the bottle. The blowing head then rises, lifting the blank mould away from the glass in the pot. Any glass trailing out of the hole at the bottom is cut off by the rapid stroke of a knife.

A puff of compressed air is then forced into the initial opening or "mouth", which has been enlarged by the plunger into a cavity that presses the shoulders of the blank tightly against the inside surfaces of the blank mould. The blank mould opens, leaving the blank hanging by the grip of the neck moulds. In the meantime the unit

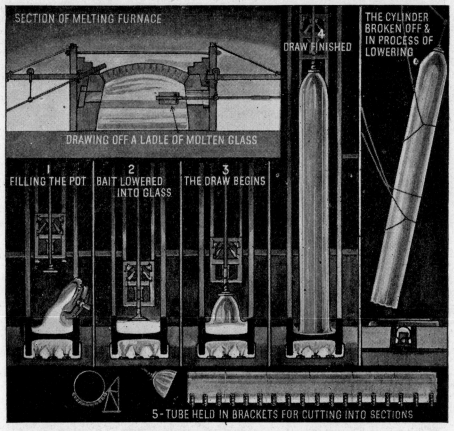

SECTION OF MELTING FURNACE

4
DRAW FINISHED

THE CYLINDER
BROKEN OFF &
IN PROCESS OF
LOWERING

DRAWING OFF A LADLE OF MOLTEN GLASS

1
FILLING THE POT

2
BAIT LOWERED
INTO GLASS

3
THE DRAW BEGINS

5 - TUBE HELD IN BRACKETS FOR CUTTING INTO SECTIONS

CYLINDRICAL DRAWING OF SHEETS

Fig. 10. *Sheet glass was formerly made by drawing long cylinders as shown here, then cutting them open and flattening out under heat. The method is not often used nowadays.*

has moved away from the pot of molten glass, and there is space for another pair of moulds to rise from below and embrace the hanging blank. These moulds represent the finished form of the bottle and the blank is blown out into them by a further supply of compressed air. When this has been done the bottle is released and ejected from the machine just in time to release the moulds to accommodate the next blank.

The knife can be adjusted under the parison mould to the greatest nicety without the use of a spanner. The blowing cams are in small segments, and may be adjusted by hand in any direction while the machine is running, so that it is unnecessary to stop the machine in case the blowing of any unit has to be altered. There are sixty-four of these cam segments, each consisting of ten tiers.

On dual moulds—that is to say, with two sets of moulds on each unit—a week's production of quart bottles is estimated at 4,200 gross. In one works alone, one furnace and its attendant machines produce 35,000 tumblers per machine per day. This machine can produce 1,100 gross of 16 oz. jars per day, or over 1,000,000 jars a week (Fig. 17).

Let us turn again to the window. The miles and miles of glass in houses and shops are now not generally made by the crown glass method described above. Instead, they come from gigantic machines fed by a constant river of molten glass. Although the materials used—sand, soda and lime—are the same as in the early days, the extent of the progress made in a little over two centuries is well illustrated by the fact that the largest mirror known in England in 1716 measured 86 in. by 44 in., whereas a sheet made in recent years measured 400 in. by 150 in. (Fig. 14).

In the manufacture of sheet glass, the melting process takes place in three stages. First there is the initial melting —that is, the chemical reaction between the three ingredients—which results in a sticky mass full of bubbles. The second stage is the "fining" operation, in which the temperature is raised so that the glass loses its viscous nature and becomes watery, thus allowing the gases forming the bubbles to rise to the surface; at this stage the glass is so thin that it is quite unworkable. Finally the glass is cooled down to the correct consistency for working.

The glass is melted in a tank like a swimming bath. It may be as large as 120 ft. in length by 36 ft. wide and 5 ft. deep; the sides and bottom are made of clay blocks and the roof of silica bricks. Such a tank may contain anything up to 900 tons of molten glass, with temperatures varying from 1,200° C. to 1,450° C., in different parts.

Having obtained the molten glass, the problem now is to make a sheet. The method used to be to treat it like toffee—to pour it on to a slab. Molten

MOLTEN GLASS EMERGING FROM THE ROLLERS

Fig. 11. *Having been heated in a gas-fired furnace to a temperature of about 1,600° C., the molten glass passes between rollers. When cool it is polished with rouge and water.*

glass was taken from a tank in a ladle, poured on to a smooth cast-iron table, and then rolled out into a sheet by means of a travelling roller. This method has now been superseded by a process in which the 'metal'—molten glass—flows direct from the drawing end of the tank between rollers into the annealing lehr in a continuous ribbon of glass.

RIBBED ROOF GLASS

Although a sheet of glass made in this way is quite suitable for places where it is merely a question of admitting light, the glass is semi-obscured by having come in contact with the roller and the casting table. Such glass—particularly plain rolled glass—is used extensively for roof glazing because it breaks up the direct rays of the sun.

One trouble with the old crown glass window was that it could only be made in small panes. An advance was made in this respect by the hand cylinder process, in which the glass was blown in the form of a cylinder and then flattened. This was followed by the cylinder-drawn process (Fig. 10), in which the glass was ladled from the tank into a double-sided crucible or pot contained in a kiln heated by producer gas. A pipe with a re-entrant lip was lowered into the glass which solidified as it welled over the edge of the lip forming a solid ring by means of which the cylinder was drawn up from the pot, air being supplied to maintain the required diameter. In this way a cylinder of 30 in. diameter and 40 ft. length was drawn. At the end of the draw the cylinder was cut off from the pot and lowered on to a rest.

It then remained to cut the cylinder into lengths. This was done by means of an electrically heated wire that, in this process, took the place of a hot thread of glass used by the hand-blower. The pot from which the cylinder was drawn

was turned over so that the remains of the cylinder were melted out in the pot kiln, thus presenting a clean side of the pot for the next draw. As the cylinders drawn in this way were too wide to be flattened in one piece, they were generally split lengthwise into two, three or four sections, or "shawls".

For the flattening, the cylinder was usually placed on a carriage and introduced into the back of the flattening kiln, where it was warmed up until nearly soft. It was then lifted from the carriage on to the flattening stone, opened out and rubbed down with a piece of wood, known as the "polissoir", which was kept wet; the idea being that when the sheet was rubbed, the hot glass produced a buffer of steam between itself and the wood, so that the sheet was not scratched because the polissoir never came into actual contact with the glass. After flattening, the sheet travelled down an annealing lehr and was dipped in warm water in order to remove the scum generally formed from the sulphur in the gases in the lehr.

FLAT SHEET DRAWING

These processes of blowing the cylinder involve several operations, and for many years attempts were made to improve on them by drawing a flat sheet in the first instance. The difficulty in doing this is to maintain the width of the sheet. It has been found that if a "bait" in the form of a sheet of metal is dipped into molten glass, the glass adheres to the bait. As the bait is drawn up, the glass is drawn with it in the form of a sheet, but this gradually narrows until finally only a thread is left.

There are three successful methods of overcoming this difficulty. The first, invented in Belgium by Emile Fourcault and perfected in 1914, was developed and improved by the American Libbey-Owens process, shown in Fig. 13. Both

MODERN SHEET DRAWING

Fig. 12. *Practically all sheet glass is made by the drawing process as here shown. Continuously moving, the glass solidifies, anneals and cools, to be cut into lengths at the top. The apparatus shown may be one of nine similar heads at the same furnace.*

these methods, however, have technical defects which are overcome in the process known as the Pittsburgh process. In this method the width of the sheet is maintained by a mechanism consisting of a fork and a pair of knurled air-cooled rollers. The fork—a slightly curved steel plate with a slot in it—is placed just above the level of the molten glass at the drawing end of the tank, so that the ribbon of glass flows through the slot and is engaged at its edges by the knurled rollers. These are pressed towards each other in order to grip the glass; they cool the edges of the sheet and prevent it "waisting". The point of formation of the sheet is maintained by means of a fireclay bar in which there is a slit which is sunk below the surface of the metal to act as an anchor. The sheet is solidified quickly by water coolers, then passed between asbestos-covered rollers through an annealing tower (Fig. 12).

In its journey direct from the tank, up the cooling tower, the glass does not come into contact with any solid material until it is quite rigid; it, there-

fore, retains its fire-finished surface quite unspoiled. The sheet is cut off by an electrically-heated cutter that travels with the sheet (Fig. 15). By the old process a worker could produce 160 sq. ft. an hour. The machine-blown cylinder process gives about 750 sq. ft. per hour. At 60 in. per minute the Libbey-Owens machine will produce at the rate of 1,250 sq. ft. per hour, or 30,000 sq. ft. in 24 hours. In the Pittsburgh process it is not unusual to draw 100 miles of glass non-stop.

The modern flat-drawn processes produce glass that is good enough for most windows, since it gives clear vision. Yet there is always a certain amount of distortion, however, because the sheet is not perfectly flat. Clear vision can be obtained only through glass of which both surfaces are perfectly flat and parallel. To make such glass—that is, plate glass—it must be rolled into a sheet, annealed, ground and polished.

Until very recently, polished plate glass was made by melting the frit—the mixture of sand, soda, saltcake and limestone—in fireclay pots, each holding

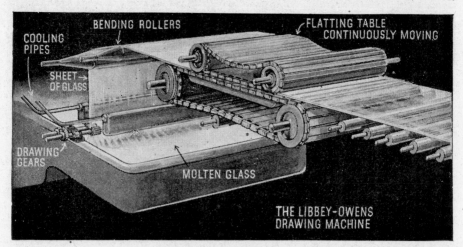

DRAWING A FLAT SHEET OF GLASS

Fig. 13. *The Libbey-Owens modification of the Fourcault drawing machine for sheet glass. The sheet of glass, while still hot, is bent over rollers on to a horizontal track.*

MODERN EXAMPLE OF PROGRESS

Fig. 14. *This giant sheet of glass exemplifies the strides made in recent years. But though methods change the basic materials used—soda, sand and lime—remain the same.*

approximately a ton of molten metal. This was heated for 17 hours in a gas-fired furnace at a temperature of approximately 1,600° C. At the end of that time mechanical tongs gripped the pots and conveyed them to the iron casting tables, on which the molten glass was slowly poured. A roller covering the whole width of the table then moved across it, flattening the molten metal into a plate, the thickness being regulated by adjustable guides at the side of the casting table (Fig. 11). The glass was translucent but not transparent, its surface being rough and coarse, although the inside was crystal clear. After it had been annealed it was ground, the rough surface being smoothed down on rotating circular tables by means of revolving ironshod disks, the abrasive being sand or emery, and

water. Then the plate was polished on both sides by means of felt-padded disks, the polishing agent being rouge and water.

About 1921 a new process was introduced. In this, the Bicheroux process, the glass was melted in pots as in the old process (Fig. 3). It was then rolled between two rollers instead of being poured on to a table in front of a single roller, the result being a flatter sheet, involving less loss of time in the subsequent grinding and polishing operations.

In 1923 the Ford Motor Company introduced a new process known as the continuous flow method, in which the glass is melted in the tank, from whence it flows down a spout on to two rollers, that roll the glass in the form of a continuous ribbon down the annealing lehr.

Four complete units are used, each

CUTTING SHEET GLASS INTO LENGTHS

Fig. 15. *Having now been solidified by water coolers the sheet glass is cut into lengths, as shown here, by an electrically heated cutter at the top of the annealing tower.*

consisting of a glass-melting furnace of some 400 tons' capacity capable of melting 40 tons every 24 hours. Each also includes annealing lehrs 442 ft. in length, and 86 grinding machines and 72 polishing machines. The glass flows from the furnaces in a continuous broad ribbon at a speed of 729 ft. per minute, and is cut into lengths sufficient for three windscreens. These sections each weigh 75 lb., but when ground and polished the weight is reduced to 51 lb.

For these processes seven grades of sand are used in turn, along with copious supplies of water. As each grade of sand is used it is recovered and passed to the next lower grade to be used again and again down the scale, except in the final grinding in which a very fine grade of sand is used. From the sand-grinding machines the plates go to the emery machines, where five grades of abrasive are used. Here again, the emery is used time after time, one grade lower each time after being recovered. After being carefully inspected for defects, the plates go to the polishing machines.

The business of grinding and polishing the glass necessarily prevented the ideal "flow" of the product through the factory in an uninterrupted stream. In the process above the glass must, of course, be ground and polished on both sides; to accomplish this it must be shifted three times from one machine to another. In the process the plates are set in plaster on a large circular table some 38 feet in diameter, the entire surface of the table being covered with glass. For the grinding, the table is

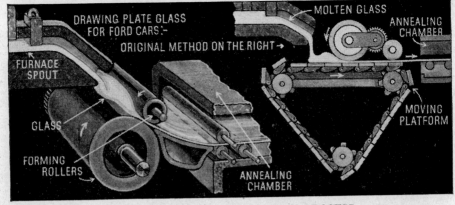

DRAWING BY THE PILKINGTON PROCESS

Fig. 16. *Right: The first Ford machine for drawing continuously. Left: the later modification. The machines, which extend to hundreds of feet, include polishing apparatus.*

rotated under two large cast-iron revolving runners which apply the abrasive; then the glass goes to polishing machines similar in principle but with cast-iron runners replaced by felt runners.

A process used by the Ford Motor Works for the rapid polishing of plate glass for motor-car windscreens was invented by Pilkington Bros. Ltd., to roll a sheet wide enough to cut plate glass of the largest sizes (Fig. 16). The Pilkington plant does away with the need for shifting the glass from machine to machine. It secures the uninterrupted flow of a stream of plate glass from the tank to the warehouse, where it arrives in a polished state without handling, having been ground and polished on both sides simultaneously.

Instead of having to be transferred to rotating tables, the sheets emerge from the rollers on to a very ingenious arrangement of tables which move in a continuous straight line. These tables,

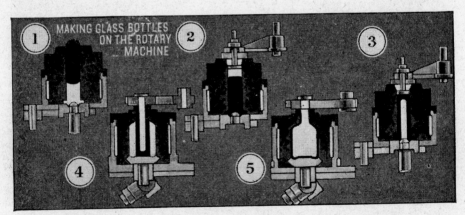

STAGES IN THE MACHINE-BLOWING OF GLASS BOTTLES

Fig. 17. (1) *A charge of glass drawn into mould;* (2) *Blown to bottom;* (3) *First blow into cylinder;* (4) *Blank withdrawn and inserted into bottle mould;* (5) *Fully blown into mould.*

TESTING AND INSPECTING SAFETY GLASS

Fig. 18. *For some years past the law has insisted on all motor cars being fitted with non-splintering glass, which is a kind of sandwich composed of transparent plastic material, or metal, enclosed in two sheets of glass. A view of the final testing and inspecting conveyor— note the drop hammer from which every finished sheet receives a heavy blow.*

HANDLING PLATE GLASS

Until toughened glass comes into general use there will always be a danger of breakage, but modern methods have reduced to a minimum the risk and labour of moving large sheets of plate glass from one part of the factory to another. The picture shows a transport crane and suction apparatus raising a sheet to be lowered gently on to the works trolley.

E.T.T.S.—B

which butt together in an endless succession and carry the glass under a series of grinders and polishers, fit together so accurately that they give a perfectly continuous bed on which the glass can be laid without any regard to the joints between them. The grinding heads are cast iron; sand and water are used, as in the case of the disk grinding, coarse sand being fed to the first grinders, and then finer and finer sand until, as the glass leaves the last of the grinders, it is ground flat and smooth. As the glass proceeds, it is carefully washed and then passed underneath the polishers, where it is polished with rouge and water.

SAFETY GLASS

We have seen how a few of the more ordinary forms of glass are made. There are many special kinds that embody interesting features of manufacture. British law now insists that all motorcars shall be fitted with "safety" glass which will not fly in splinters when it is smashed. This is a kind of compound glass—a sandwich of a transparent plastic material firmly held between two thin outer sheets of glass. Another type of safety glass is made by embedding wire-netting into a sheet of glass during the course of manufacture. The glass is poured in front of the main roller, as in the case of ordinary rolled plate; wire netting is then fed to a roller with a fluted surface. These fins or flutes force the netting into the hot sheet of glass, the surface of the glass being smoothed by two smaller following rollers.

In a third method the plate is rolled to the ultimate thickness required and the wire pressed into it whilst the glass is still plastic; and in a fourth the wire is fixed on to the rolling table at an exact height and the glass is poured on.

All of us—except, perhaps, the glassmakers—wish that glass were less fragile; but tumblers and the like that can tumble without hurting themselves are no novelty. It has long been known that glass could be tempered and made stronger by quenching it, when just set, in hot oil. Glass tempered or toughened in this way has been extensively used for such articles as boiler gauges, but it is only recently that a process has been developed in France by which large sheets can be toughened. The sheets are suspended vertically in an electric furnace until the glass is soft but not soft enough to lose its shape; it is then suddenly cooled by blowing air on both sides. The surfaces immediately harden whilst the inside of the sheet is still hot and soft. As the inside of the sheet cools, it contracts, placing the outside layers in compression, and producing a sheet that is much stronger mechanically.

Not only is toughened glass very much stronger than ordinary glass; when it is broken, it breaks in a very different way, cracking all over and disintegrating into small fragments. These fragments have not the dangerous cutting edges of ordinary glass and can be handled without fear of cuts.

ARMOUR-PLATE GLASS

One type of this toughened glass, known as "armour-plate", is made by Pilkington Bros. Ltd. This glass has undergone a heat treatment and has become so toughened that it will bend, twist, resist hard knocks or high temperature (Fig. 18). One advantage of armour-plate glass is that, as the toughening process in no way affects the quality, satisfactory vision is maintained and there is no fear of discoloration or distortion.

Glass bricks are coming into fashion, and we are waiting only for bold architects to put them to all the uses of the more conventional building materials. The city of glass foreseen by fiction-writers may yet become a reality.

FURNITURE

Raw Materials. Seasoning. Setting Out and Marking Out. Workshop Machinery. Cabinet-Making. The Carcase. Plywood. Decoration. Carving. The Windsor Chair. Finishing. Upholstery. Springing and Stuffing.

G o to any great furniture factory, and you will find the air full of the sound of the rotary saw, the automatic planing machine, the mortising and tenoning and the dovetailing machine. In big workshops these machines, power-driven, operated by skilled machinists, are to be seen by the score; but nevertheless, furniture-making really begins in the forests. Here, in stalwart trees of many kinds, we have the raw material of furniture, timber.

Next, with axe and saw, comes the woodman who fells the trees that are destined for commercial use. Ideally the wood should then be sawn up into baulks, planks and other sizes on the spot and there seasoned. In practice, however, it is often necessary for the logs to travel thousands of miles from the forest to the sawmill. In Canada, for example, you can see the unseasoned logs being floated down the St. Lawrence in their thousands, and similar sights are typical of any great timber-producing country in Europe or America.

In the sawmills the bark is removed, the timber sawn up and then stacked

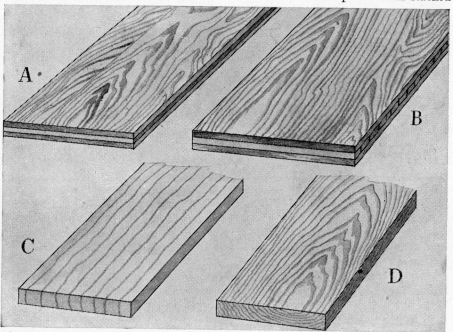

TYPES OF WOOD USED FOR FURNITURE

Fig. 1. *The cut of the timber will help to determine the character of furniture. The types of wood used in furniture making shown above are* (A) *plywood,* (B) *laminated board,* (C) *straight-grained wood, sawn radially,* (D) *figured wood, sawn across the log.*

for seasoning. There are two methods of seasoning; natural or air-drying, artificial or kiln-drying. The purpose of seasoning is to reduce the water-content of the wood to a point below that at which shrinkage takes place or fungi can attack. Kiln-drying is the better method for furniture woods, not only because it is quicker but because it is also more thorough. Either box kilns or progressive kilns are used. The planks are piled on trucks which, in the former method, remain stationary and, in the latter, move very slowly forward into progressively drier air until the seasoning process has been quite completed.

FURNITURE WOODS

In addition to oak, the timbers most commonly used for furniture-making are walnut and mahogany, but an immense range of other woods is employed to a greater or lesser extent. These are used for special articles of furniture, for inlaid decoration, for linings and interior fittings.

Among British-grown timbers sometimes made into furniture are beech, birch, elm, sycamore and maple; from other countries come such highly decorative woods as amboyna, macassar ebony, coromandel, rosewood, Indian laurel and Australian silky oak.

All these are known as hardwoods, but softwoods are also used; for example, Columbian pine and cedar. These classifications, it should be noted, give no indication of the quality of the timber. Paradoxical though it sounds, some softwoods are in actual fact quite hard and very durable while some of the hardwoods are soft and liable to perish. All timbers obtained from trees having broad leaves which are shed annually are known as hardwoods; those from trees (mostly evergreens) with needle-shaped or narrow leaves are softwoods. British timber is quite extensively used and, as English woods grow comparatively slowly, has the advantage of density and durability. Some High Wycombe manufacturers, for instance, buy an entire wood as it stands and have the trees felled and brought home to the mills by their own men.

Seasoning consists, first of all, of drying in the stack—a matter of two or three years according to the class of wood and the size to which it is cut. It is not uncommon to see great stacks of beech, elm, oak and walnut drying in the manufacturers' yards.

Then comes the passage through the heated drying chambers and, finally, in some cases the roughly-cut parts for furniture may again be subjected to the hardening effect of exposure.

The first process in the furniture factory does not involve the timber which will afterwards be used. It consists in making a full-size drawing of the piece of furniture which is to be made. The making of this drawing is known as "setting out"; it is done by the foreman or draughtsman. The drawing is executed either on stiff paper or, for preference, on a $\frac{1}{2}$ in. pine board known as a "rod". To accompany this drawing the draughtsman also compiles a "cutting list", this being a list of the timber which will be needed for the job.

MARKING OUT

Drawing and cutting lists are then handed to the marker-out who selects the necessary planks and boards and, with chalk or pencil, makes measured drawings on the timber to show the exact size and shape of each piece. Great care is necessary to obtain economical arrangement of the different parts, so that as little wood as possible is wasted. Uniformity in colour, direction of grain and figure, as well as the soundness of the timber have also to be considered. An allowance in the measurements of

HIGH-SPEED ROUTING MACHINE

Fig. 1. *One of the many labour-saving machines used nowadays in furniture making. The operative above is cutting the very intricate base board required for a sewing machine.*

$\frac{1}{8}$ in. has also to be made for saw-cutting, and an additional $\frac{1}{8}$ in. for planing and fitting. A door stile set out 2 in. wide, for example, would be marked out $2\frac{1}{4}$ in. Each piece marked out is numbered to agree with the cutting list and drawing.

When marked out the planks and boards are handed to the machine foreman, who is responsible for the cutting out and planing up.

It should be understood that in the case of high-quality craftsman's furni-ture every manufacturing process is carried out by hand, but with mass-produced commercial furniture the work is done to a very large extent by machinery. There are wonderfully efficient, electrically driven machines for edging and sawing, planing and thicknessing, mortise-and-tenoning and dovetailing, sand-papering, glue jointing, spindle moulding, panel planing and the like. Figs. 1 and 2 illustrate some typical furniture-making machines.

Sand-papering, for example, is done on a divided flat table, beneath which is a large drum revolving flush with the table-top. When the paper needs renewing on the drum, the sections of the table can be moved back.

There are also all-purpose machines which combine a band, circular and flat saws, as well as mortising, boring and moulding machines. Of necessity a machine of this description is bulky, but as it takes the place of several separate items of woodworking plant, it really effects a great saving in space.

An efficient sawing machine would be capable of a maximum feeding speed of 152 feet per minute for straight sawing and of taking timber 4 inches thick.

The parts marked out are now cut out on one of these machines and are then passed, with the drawing and cutting list, to the cabinet-maker.

This is the general procedure in furniture-making, though details vary with each job and the factory organisation.

If, for example, the article to be made were an oak bureau, the "rod" would first be drawn; the cutting list would then be made out, giving the exact measurements, the number of pieces and the kind of wood. When all the pieces have been cut they are passed, with the rod and cutting list, to the cabinet-maker. The stand is dovetailed together, with the angles braced for greater strength. The proper method for fixing all frames and rails is the mortise and tenon; a rectangular socket in one piece and a corresponding projection which fits into it on the other, these being made by the mortise-and-tenon machine already referred to. All drawers, boxes and carcase work should be dovetailed—dovetail joints are a series of interlocking wedge-shaped incisions and projections.

Inferior joins which are seen on cheap furniture are the butt joint, sometimes with and sometimes without a strengthening chamfer block, and the mitre,

MODERN FURNITURE WORKSHOP

Fig. 2. *Above is seen a view of a typical machinery workshop. The operative in the centre is at work at a planing machine; on the left a plank is being cut on a circular saw.*

ASSEMBLING THE FINISHED PRODUCT

Fig. 3. *Nowadays the parts of a piece of furniture are made separately and then assembled. Great accuracy is required in the separate parts to give a smooth fit in the finished article.*

which may or may not be strengthened by the addition of a screw if necessary.

The drawers of the bureau, as in a chest of drawers, are made slightly full at the back so that as they are drawn out they gradually tighten. The stationery case is made separately and glued into position. An opposite method is followed to that adopted with drawers, for stationery cases are made slightly *smaller* at the back.

The fall-front of the bureau is supported by slides, or lopers, which are fixed so that they draw out when the fall-front is lowered. A dowel is inserted near the back of the loper which engages against the side of the bureau to prevent the loper being drawn out completely. A strip of billiard cloth is glued to the top edge of the loper to prevent damage to the fall face when it is horizontal.

Pieces of furniture such as wardrobes, bookcases, sideboards, etc., always consist of what is called a carcase; big pieces like winged wardrobes and break-front bookcases may have as many as three carcases or even more (Figs. 3 and 5).

The carcase is really a box, which may be fitted with shelves and divided by partitions to receive doors and drawers. The construction is similar, with slight variations, in all carcase work.

First the timber is sawn to the correct dimensions and planed up, and then dovetails are sawn, all this being done nowadays by machinery. The carcase is then knocked together dry. If the result is satisfactory it is taken to pieces again and the dovetail joints are glued and driven home, this being done by placing

INTERIOR OF A TYPICAL

Fig. 4. *Not the least important process in furniture making is that of finishing, and french polish is still one of the most popular types of finish. Filling of the grain and two applications*

FRENCH POLISHING SHOP

of polish are required, and considerable skill and judgment are called for to estimate the time, temperature, and amount necessary to produce the well-known high, smooth polish.

E.T.T.S.—B*

a hardwood block across the dovetails and striking with a hammer in the horizontal position.

A new development in furniture manufacture which has taken place in recent years is the use of plywood. This consists of three or more sheets of wood so sawn and cemented together that the grain of each "ply" is at right-angles to that of its neighbours. Odd numbers are always used, a central board being employed as a core for cementing upon; and although three-ply sheets are commonest five- and seven-ply, and even stouter sections, are not impossible.

USE OF PLYWOOD

The chief advantages of plywood are its greater strength and its freedom from the tendency to warp or twist. The weakness of solid timber runs across the grain; the tensile strength may be twenty times as great parallel to the grain as it is across the grain. But with plywood it is true to say that as the grain runs in all directions and in none the tensile strength can be regarded as almost equal in every direction.

There is also a form of plywood known as laminated or core stock. This consists of an inner core of kiln-dried wood in small short strips, cemented together at high pressure and then closed between two plies of veneer. Laminated stock is the strongest form of timber yet available for furniture construction, having a tensile strength seven or eight times greater than that of ordinary wood.

Plywood can be worked very much like solid timber, though variations of procedure and adjustments of machinery are required; this is only to be expected in view of the great difference between plywood and solid wood. In the hands of an expert, plywood can be mortised-and-tenoned, dovetailed or dowelled. For mortise-and-tenon it is even possible to work a tongue on the

laminated core, so firmly are the core strips cemented; while for dovetailing it is necessary only to make the dovetails of equal size and rather larger than is customary in solid wood. Sharp tools are needed for this.

One very important result of the use of plywood is that panels can be much larger than with solid wood; if the plywood is of good quality and properly seasoned, such panels can be relied on not to warp or twist. The mouldings with which the panelling is framed are also much less important. With plywood, the structural strength being in the panel, the mouldings are merely supplementary and a protection to the edges. On the other hand, with old-time period furniture all the strength was in the mouldings and not in the panel. This represents a constructional revolution. Whereas in period furniture the panels are recessed and their importance secondary, in modern furniture they are either flush or in relief and their structural importance is fundamental.

VENEERING

For centuries it has been the practice to decorate furniture by the process known as veneering, i.e. the application of thin sheets of handsomely figured wood to the exterior surfaces. Veneers are obtained either by sawing the timber with a circular saw, in much the same manner as bacon is cut into rashers; "peeling" or knife-cutting, by rotating the wood against the edge of a knife; or, lastly, by "flat-cutting" or "slicing", this being done by a machine which, in principle, is like a giant joiner's plane. The thickness of veneers commonly varies between $\frac{3}{8}$ inch and $\frac{1}{120}$ inch according to requirements.

Before the introduction of plywood the best base for the application of veneers was solid mahogany. As this wood does not tend to re-absorb

FITTING INTO THE CARCASE

Fig. 5. *Wardrobes and similar articles consist mainly of a box called the carcase, which is made separately and into which the drawers, doors and other fittings are inserted.*

moisture readily it is free from the tendencies to warp or split, which have a disastrous effect on surface veneers.

With plywood, however, the veneers glued together are their own base: or rather, the base is provided by the centre ply.

Veneers are fixed by first covering the base with glue, spread either by hand or by machine, which is then allowed to attain the right consistency. Then the veneer is laid upon it and the whole is inserted in a press (Figs. 7 and 8). Either cold or hot presses may be used. The retaining boards, or cauls, are made of Oregon pine plywood for cold and zinc or aluminium for hot pressing.

Forms of decoration which are often used in combination with veneering are inlay and marquetry.

Inlay was originally the process of cutting into solid wood and filling the resultant cavities with pieces of other woods or other materials, such as silver, ivory, mother-of-pearl or brass. Inlay is now frequently used with veneers (for example, a contrasting border to a plywood panel) in which case the process is similar to marquetry.

Marquetry is employed to cover an entire surface with a variety of woods in a closely fitting and often pictorial pattern. The first step in the construction of a piece of marquetry is the making of an accurate working drawing of the design. It is thence transferred to tracing paper by being carefully pricked out and is again transferred to stout white paper by rubbing brown marking powder through the perforations. By following these pouce marks the paper is then cut up into the numerous small

MARQUETRY CUTTING

Fig. 6. *A band saw which can be adjusted to cut in any direction helps in this highly skilled operation.*

pieces of the design; the paper cut-outs are then placed upon veneers and fixed down with paste or weak glue. They are next cut out on a hand-operated machine known as a "donkey", which resembles an elaborate fret-saw. (*See* Fig. 6.)

The ground veneer which is to receive the pieces of marquetry is cut out in the same way, great care being taken not to split or break the veneer. The veneer and the inlays are now pieced together. First, the ground veneer is lightly glued to a sheet of paper and the pieces previously prepared are then glued into the remaining spaces.

Finally, the surface of the whole panel is coated with glue and covered with a sheet of strong paper, which is kept under heavy pressure until the glue is set. The first paper is then removed from the other side of the panel. The surface now visible which, as the finished work, was the underside of the panel when in course of construction becomes the underside once more when the panel is laid in its final position. Good marquetry is one of the supreme achievements in the decoration of furniture.

Another type of decoration which was formerly lavished on period furniture, but has almost disappeared to-day, is carving. Many fine Chippendale chairs, for example, literally consist of carving; in fact, if the carving were taken away the furniture would no longer be there.

Carving is a highly skilled handicraft akin to sculpture, though on present-day furniture it is frequently imitated by machinery. Sometimes the first stages, or roughing out, are done by a rapidly revolving cutter, after which the work is handed to carvers to finish. Plastic wood which has been shaped in metal moulds under great pressure is also used; the results are really wood castings, which are glued into position. Another method with applied carvings is to cut out the pattern with a fret-saw from planed wood of the right thickness to give the desired relief, and afterwards to glue it firmly in place and to finish off the detail by hand.

Unfortunately, carving, which can be one of the glories of exclusive and expensive pieces, is essentially a hand process and not commercially practicable for cheap mass-produced furniture.

CHAIR-MAKING

It has long been a tradition of the furniture industry that chair-making is a separate craft from cabinet-making; it includes settees, upholstered armchairs, couches and divans.

Chair-making is a complex craft which requires long practice and wide experience if the craftsman is to attain both skill and versatility. This will be realised by anyone who considers the innumerable types of chairs in existence and their astonishing diversity of character. The tendency, of course, is for the craftsman to specialise in certain types. One of the most widely known is the traditional Windsor which, for generations, has been made in and around the town of High Wycombe.

The first processes in the construction of a Windsor chair are carried out in the actual beech wood. Cutting is done in winter, when the sap is dry and the chair-turner works in a hut in the glades. The timber used for the legs and spars is known colloquially as "clothes props". These are cut into the requisite lengths and turned on a simple pole lathe which is made to revolve by means of a treadle, the turning being done with a chisel in the ordinary way.

After the legs, spars and spindles have been made, the seat is shaped by hand with an adze. A rectangular piece of wood cut from an elm plank is used and the seat is made with a wood tail-piece which receives two diagonal spars.

THE VENEER PRESS

Fig. 8. *Glue is spread on the base and the veneer laid on it, and the whole goes into the press, which may be cold or hot.*

VENEER ASSEMBLY

Fig. 7. *Pieces of veneer are laid face upwards and held together by means of strips of paper glued on to them.*

After being roughly shaped with the adze, it is finished off with a spokeshave.

The banister for the wheelback is next cut out to the traditional pattern with a fret-saw and smoothed off with a rasp. When the legs and stretchers have been fixed to the chair bottom, the upright spindles for the back and the central banister are put into position. Two or more spindles, to act as stretchers between the tail-piece and the bow that crowns the back, are next inserted and then the final piece of work is to key the whole superstructure together.

The task of making the characteristic bow for the back of the chair deserves a few lines of description to itself. Ash or yew is used. A piece of wood is sawn off a selected length of timber of the correct thickness and, having been boiled and steamed until pliable, is forced into a metal horse-collar and confined in that mould until it has become thoroughly set and seasoned. The bow is finished with a spokeshave and given the conventional line in a vice. The whole process is shown in Fig. 9.

Finishing, as its name implies, is the last process. It is a very important one and nowadays a number of alternative treatments are available. The simplest method is to leave the wood in its natural state, without any sort of staining, and to polish with a compound of raw beeswax and turpentine. By partly filling the pores of the wood, the wax gives a protective finish to the wood which can be improved by rubbing.

FUMING

Oak furniture is sometimes finished by the method known as fuming. Before being assembled, the various parts are put in an air-tight chamber with two or three wide-mouthed utensils each of which contains from a pint to a quart of .880 deg. ammonia. The fumes impart a deep brown tone to the oak, which is afterwards polished. The time taken depends on the strength and quantity of ammonia and the colour desired.

Yet another method for treating oak is known as liming. Well-flaked quick-lime is mixed with water to the density of a thick paint. The lime is applied quickly and evenly to the surface of the oak with a flat brush. This turns the wood to a greyish brown and the longer the lime is allowed to remain the darker will be the effect. When the dry lime has been removed with a stiff wire brush the minute lime particles which remain in the pores of the wood give the characteristic silvery-grey effect.

Staining can be employed with practically any timber and a number of chemical stains are used. They include water stains, spirit stains and oil stains. Bichromate of potash is used extensively. The stain may be applied with a brush, rag or sponge, or sprayed on.

With French polishing, the first process is filling the grain of the wood, this being necessary to obtain a smooth, even surface. The filler, consisting of either plaster or what is known as American patent filler, is well rubbed into the grain and left to harden. If plaster is used this has to be "killed", i.e. made invisible, by the application of linseed oil which also gives greater transparency to the subsequent coating of polish.

Next, a coat of polish consisting of shellac dissolved in methylated spirit is applied. A pad of cotton wool is saturated with the shellac polish and covered with a linen rag which acts as a filter and distributes the polish evenly. The polish is applied with a circular motion and considerable pressure to force it into the wood. The work having been left, so that the polish can sink in and harden, is then rubbed down with fine sandpaper or pumice powder, after which the shellac polish is again applied (Fig. 4).

French polishing is largely a matter of individual judgment. The oil has to be applied sparingly or it may be sweated out, for the whole effect of the process is greatly dependent on atmospheric conditions and temperature.

CELLULOSE POLISHING

Cellulose polishing is also employed. The lacquers used consist of either nitro-cellulose or cellulose acetate dissolved in suitable solvents such as acetone, amyl acetate or butyl acetate. Petrol or benzol is also included for quick drying. Cellulose lacquers are applied by the use of a spray pistol.

These are the essential processes involved in the making of furniture when the material used is timber. Other materials which will almost certainly come into more widespread use in the future are steel, aluminium, glass and various plastics; these, however, will

MAKING A WINDSOR CHAIR

Fig. 9. (A) *Adzing out the seat;* (B) *Turning the leg with a pole lathe;* (C) *Fixing the legs;* (D) *Finishing the seat with a spokeshave;* (E) *Finishing the arched back;* (F) *Cutting out the triangular holes in the wheel-backed banister;* (G) *Fitting the spars from arch to tailpiece.*

naturally require their own techniques of construction and decoration.

Upholstery is such a specialised branch of furniture-making that it may justly be regarded as a separate craft. The word is derived from the verb "to uphold", upholsterers being first known as "upholders" and then as "upholdsters". Originally these words denoted a broker who held up goods to public view, but in modern speech the literal meaning of "to upholster" is "to furnish furniture with stuffing, springs, etc." This definition applies more particularly to chairs and settees.

The earliest examples of upholstery in English furniture date from Jacobean times, but in the course of rather more than two hundred years an immense development in the craft has taken place. Carolean high-backed chairs had flat removable cushions, but eighteenth-century armchairs were stuffed with wool and horse-hair, the latter still being the best material for filling. In Victorian times armchairs had a large coiled iron spring in the seat, which gave resilience until it either broke or became dislodged, when it became useless.

Modern armchairs and settees are sprung quite differently. They are built on a scientific principle known as "multiple spiral springing"; instead of one spring they have many (Fig. 12). These springs are so arranged that weight is distributed over them as evenly as possible and risk of breakage is thus reduced to a minimum; as they are tied in it is exceedingly difficult for any of the springs to get out of place.

THE CHAIR FRAME SHOP

Fig. 10. *Chairs, like most other pieces of furniture, are made nowadays by mass production in parts and assembled later. In the workshop above the chair frames are being made.*

UPHOLSTERING

Fig. 11. *Upholstery is such a specialised branch of furniture making that it is almost a separate craft. Above, a settee with the springs in position ready for the canvas cover.*

In addition to the springs, the materials used in upholstery include webbing and canvas, upholsterers' twine and cord, various materials for stuffing, unbleached calico and, lastly, the outside covering material and trimmings. The tools used include upholsterers' stitching and bayonet needles, which are pointed at both ends and vary in length from 8 in. to 18 in.; bent needles for putting on cord and sewing in springs; regulators for getting stuffing material into position; web strainers for tautening webbing; stuffing cards for teasing and loosening up stuffing.

After the wooden framework has been constructed in the woodwork shop, the first process in upholstery is that of fixing bands of webbing across the underside of the seat frame. The webbing is interlaced so that it forms a lattice. Next the springs are spaced uniformly over the webbing and fastened down securely with stitches of thin, strong string known as "laid cord"; they are then lashed together and secured to the chair frame. In high class upholstery the spiral springs are sometimes held together by metal links and sometimes fixed to a finely woven wire mesh known as lace web springing. In appearance this is not unlike a woven wire mattress and generally rests on a foundation of metal strips. This, of course, eliminates the need for webbing. Moreover, the springs are sometimes in two layers, a group of lighter springs being superimposed on a group of heavier ones, the result being greater resilience and reliability. (*See* Fig. 11.)

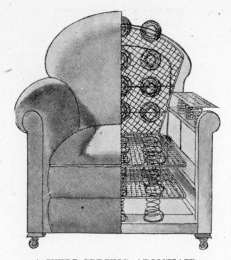

A WELL-SPRUNG ARMCHAIR

Fig. 12. *The above view shows the spiral and lace web springing of a good armchair.*

Next the springs are covered with scrim, or canvas, and the first stuffing of horsehair or fibre is spread evenly and packed closely. It is then covered with canvas as before and is second-stuffed with horsehair or fibre, and two or three layers of wadding. Lastly, all this is covered smoothly with canvas. The same treatment is adopted for the back and arms.

Excepting in the case of buttoned work (now, however, rarely seen) the whole chair, if it is of good quality workmanship, is then given a covering of calico, after which it receives its final covering material and is finished off with appropriate braid and fringes.

The springs used are steel, coated with copper; this prevents them from rusting and rotting the webbing and canvas with which they come in contact. Sometimes they are further covered with a moisture-proof braid. The shape of upholstery springs approximates to that of an hour-glass, the reason being that, when they are compressed, the coils do not rub together or "chatter".

A variety of materials are used for the stuffing, the best and most reliable being horsehair which has been subjected to superheated steam. This treatment not only sterilises the hair but causes it to curl, giving greater resilience. Wool flock is also used; this is perhaps the best substitute for horsehair as a material for the second stuffing. There are also several vegetable fibres. The best known and most reliable of these is kapok, which is the seed hair of a Javanese plant; in addition to being soft and silky it also possesses the advantage of retaining its resiliency. Cotton linters are also used, but cotton is somewhat hard in use, especially for stuffing chair seats.

Algerian grass and coir, or coconut fibre, are used as substitutes for horsehair in lower grade upholstery and are employed for first stuffing work. Woodwool, consisting of thin strip wood shavings, is another material used for both first and second stuffings; not infrequently it is mixed with hair and flock.

COVERING MATERIALS

For the final covering there is an immense range of materials from which to choose. These include leather and imitation leather, tapestries and damasks, velvets, moquettes, repps, and printed materials such as chintz.

From the nature of the work, upholstery has always been and doubtless must long remain a handicraft. This is still true in spite of the increasing use of steel mesh springing. It calls for apprenticeship, for skill can only be acquired through patient practice.

Lastly, if you would test the quality of the springing in an upholstered chair or settee, remove the loose cushions and try sitting down. Also, try pressing the seat back with the hand. Good springs are soft and resilient; inferior springs, on the other hand, are hard and unyielding.

LAMPS AND VALVES

*How a Lamp Bulb Works. Making the Flanges. Lead-in Wires. The Tungsten
Filament. Glass-Blowing and Frosting. Assembling the Bulb. Exhausting.
Wireless Valves. Fluorescent Discharge Tubes. "Cold Light."*

WHEN a current of electricity is made to flow through a wire, the wire becomes hot. The degree of heat will depend on the strength of the electric current, the thickness of the wire, and the metal of which it is made, for some metals resist the passage of electricity more than others. A strong current passing through a stout wire of low resistance may make it only slightly warm; whereas a weak current passing through a fine wire of high resistance will make it very hot indeed. Think of the filament in your torch bulb; it is made white hot even by the small amount of electricity generated in a dry battery of the familiar "number 8" type.

When a strong electric current is passed through a high-resistance wire

MAKING THE FLANGES

Fig. 1. *Glass tubing is made in 160 ft. lengths, which are cut into 4 ft. lengths and fed into flanging machines. Above, the 160 feet of glass tube is seen leaving the furnace.*

51

DUPLEX FLANGING MACHINE
Fig. 2. *In this machine four-foot lengths of glass tubing are cut into flanges at the rate of 1,200 per hour.*

surrounded by air, the wire gets hotter and hotter, the oxygen in the air carbonises the metal which, at last melts or burns to ash. If, however, the wire is enclosed in a glass bulb from which all air has been removed, it continues to get hot only up to a point at which there is a balance between the metal's resistance and the strength of the current. When that point has been reached the temperature of the wire will remain fixed so long as the current continues to flow.

An electric lamp bulb consists, in essence, of a coil of wire enclosed in a glass bulb which is evacuated of all air, the electrical resistance of the wire being such that a current of the right voltage will keep it glowing at white heat. In theory, this is a very simple idea, but difficulties of all sorts have to be overcome to put it into practice. To give but one example: very few kinds of metal can be welded to glass with an air-tight join, and those metals which can be so treated are not themselves of the right kind to glow when an electric current flows through them.

Before electric lamps could be made commercially, a great deal of research had to be undertaken to find metals which would remain white-hot for long periods without losing their strength; others had to be found which could be welded to glass quickly and would convey current from the outside of a sealed glass bulb to the inside, after all the air had been removed from it. Means then had to be found of performing mechanically the very complicated series of operations necessary to produce electric light bulbs at prices within the reach of everybody.

This is how it is done. Molten lead glass is made into tubes (Fig. 1) by pouring it on to a rotating cylinder of fireclay while a jet of air is forced through the centre. The diameter of this glass tube is approximately $\frac{3}{4}$ inch, and it is usually made in 160-foot lengths, which are subsequently cut into shorter sections, each of them four feet long.

MAKING THE FLANGES

Each of these four-foot lengths of glass tubing is now fed into an automatic machine called a "flanging machine" (Fig. 2). This heats up the free end of the tube until the glass is soft and spins it out to about one inch; the tube is then cut off to a length of about $1\frac{1}{2}$ inches. Thus each four-foot length of tubing is sufficient to make 32 flanges. Each flanging machine turns out about 1,200 flanges per hour.

The lead-in wires (Fig. 3) are one of the most ingenious features of an electric lamp. As already explained, they must be welded to the bulb so as to preclude the possibility of air entering into it. In the early days of lamp manufacture, the only suitable material known was

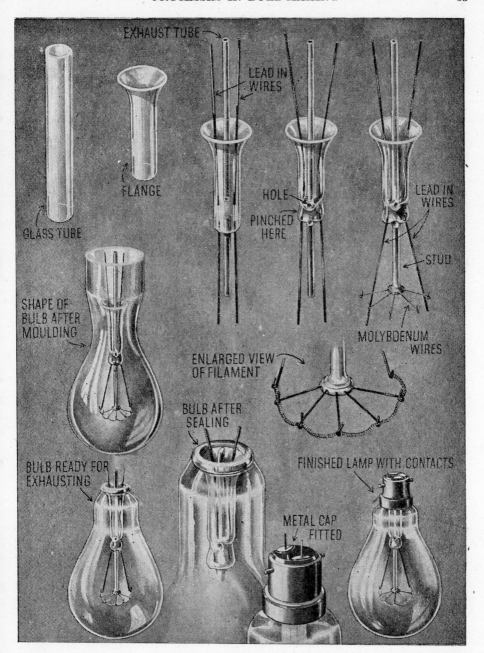

HOW A BULB IS MADE

Fig. 3. *Here are shown the various processes in the manufacture of an electric bulb. The lead-in wires are inserted, the filament is attached, and the whole put into the bulb, which is exhausted and sealed. When the metal cap and contacts are fitted it is ready for use.*

platinum, which was not only extremely expensive but would make a sealed joint only with some special kinds of glass. After persistent efforts to find a substitute, an alloy was at last made which would "seal" as well as platinum and could be used with many different kinds of glass. This alloy is produced by a combination of nickel and iron, electro-plated with copper.

LEAD-IN WIRES

The glass flange, whose manufacture is described above, forms that part of an electric bulb which conveys two lead-in wires from the contact points in the base of the lamp to the filament. Each lead-in wire consists of three distinct parts welded together: (1) a length of copper wire to carry the current from the cap contacts to the glass; (2) a short length of copper-coated nickel-iron alloy wire to pass through the glass, into which it is welded; and (3) a length of nickel wire to support the filament and also to convey the current to it. The next step in manufacture therefore consists in passing two lead-in wires through the glass flange, together with a length of thin glass tube, which will later be used to draw out the air from the bulb, and a length of glass rod which will form the central support for the filament.

ASSEMBLING THE PARTS

This operation is performed by a "pinching machine", which holds all the parts we have described in the correct positions for assembly. They are then heated at the point where they meet until they become plastic, when a pair of metal moulds presses them together and welds them in position. Although everything else must be air-tight at this point, it is necessary to keep the inner end of the exhaust tube open, so a puff of air is blown into the other end whilst the glass at the

"pinch" is still molten. This forces a clear passage through.

When all this has been done, heat is applied to the end of the glass rod; this rod is then pressed out into the form of a stud, and while it is still soft molybdenum wires are pressed into it to form supports for the filament. At the same time, these wires are cut to length and looped at the ends, and the nickel lead-in wires are bent outwards to their correct positions. The half-completed lamp is now ready for the tungsten filament to be fitted; and this is, of all the components of an electric lamp, the most difficult to produce.

MAKING THE FILAMENT

Tungsten is a metallic element obtained from an ore called "scheelite" which is imported from Australia; pure tungsten is extracted from this ore in the form of a black powder. Under powerful hydraulic pressure, this powder is compressed into ingots each about 8 inches long by $\frac{1}{4}$ inch square. The ingots are raised to a high temperature in hydrogen by a very powerful electric current, which causes the particles to adhere together, and the tungsten becomes a solid metal bar. This bar is then gradually worked into a thin, tough rod by repeated mechanical hammerings, or "swagings", as they are called. The rod is then reduced to any required diameter by drawing it through a graduated series of diamond dies, each having a central hole slightly smaller than the last. As it is pulled through these holes in succession, the tungsten wire is gradually drawn finer and finer.

A yard of tungsten wire, 1 millimetre in diameter (that is about $\frac{1}{26}$th of an inch) has to be drawn out to a length of $5\frac{1}{2}$ miles before it becomes sufficiently thin to be used for the finest filaments, which are approximately four ten-

FROSTING BULBS

Fig. 4. *General view of a pearl frosting machine. The frosting acid is forced up by air pressure from the tanks below into the bulbs which are suspended upside down above them.*

thousandths of an inch in diameter. When the tungsten is of the requisite fineness it is coiled on a mandrel into the form of an extremely fine spiral spring; it is then ready to be cut into lengths of "filament". The mounting of filaments on to their supports in the lamp is always performed by very delicate machinery. When the filament is in position its ends are electrically welded or clamped to the lead-in wires.

The internal structure of an electric lamp is then complete and ready for the glass bulb to be fitted over it. These bulbs are made entirely by automatic machinery of the most ingenious kind. Each machine does the work of twenty-four human glass-blowers, producing as many as 50,000 bulbs a day.

At one end of the machine is a furnace of molten glass. The machine's suction arms gather from this furnace a definite quantity of glass; they then place it on blow-pipes which blow out the glass and shape it in cast-iron moulds. The finished bulbs are now annealed, gauged, tested and washed. If they are to be used for lamps of the familiar "frosted" type, they must be sprayed internally with acid, washed, sprayed a second time, washed again and finally dried. This work also is done on automatic machines, each of which is able to frost up to as many as 10,000 bulbs an hour (Fig. 4).

When all this preliminary work has been done, the glass bulb is ready to be slipped over the internal fittings, which

ON THESE MACHINES BULBS ARE SEALED AFTER

Fig. 5. *The neck of each bulb is heated at a point level with the flange, and the hot glass shrinks into contact, and fuses with the end of the flange. The unwanted excess glass*

THE INTERNAL FITTINGS HAVE BEEN INSERTED
of the neck drops off, leaving the bulb sealed and ready for the process of exhausting.
This operation is carried out by automatic machines of the elaborate type shown above.

are then sealed in position within their glass covering. This operation (Fig. 5) is done by a machine which heats the neck of the bulb at a point level with the flange; the outer glass then "shrinks" or falls inwards until it makes contact with the inner flange, to which it fuses.

EXHAUSTING THE AIR

The unwanted part of the neck of the bulb now drops off, leaving a neatly sealed lamp ready for the process of "exhausting", by which all the air is removed from its interior. This operation is the most important in the whole process of lamp manufacture, because the life of a lamp that has not been properly exhausted will be short.

When the lamps are placed on the exhausting machine, the end of the exhaust tube is connected to a vacuum pump which reduces the pressure of air in each bulb until it is as nearly a vacuum as is practically possible (a perfect vacuum cannot be made). If the lamp is to be of the "vacuum" type, the exhaust tube is then heated at the point where it enters the bulb, is sealed, and the projecting part removed. Nowadays, however, most electric lamps are filled with either nitrogen or argon gas, neither of which can burn. They serve the same purpose as a vacuum and, at the same time, help to increase the length of life of the tender filament.

GAS-FILLED LAMPS

Gas-filling is done after the air has been removed, the gas entering the bulb through the exhaust tube, which is then sealed off and detached. The electric lamp whose manufacture we have been following is now complete, except for the fitting of the brass cap by which it can be attached to the socket for actual use.

Although this brass cap looks extremely simple, it is quite complicated

to make. The brass shells are stamped from sheets and the side pins are riveted electrically into the walls of the shells; the glass insulation and metal contact plates, through which the current will pass, are then inserted. The internal rim of the cap is coated with a special cement which, when baked, adheres firmly to the glass of the bulb and the brass of the cap. The copper lead-in wires from the bulb are passed through holes in the contact plates and soldered in position.

Finally, the completed lamp is tested, packed and despatched from the factory to wherever it may be required for use.

WIRELESS VALVES

Although the internal structure of a wireless valve is more complicated than that of an electric lamp bulb, and varies according to the purpose for which the valve is needed, it is essentially a lamp and is made in exactly the same manner as an ordinary bulb.

Its interior contains, in addition to a filament which is heated by the "low-tension" battery of the set, a plate of metal, through which "high tension" current can pass, and a coil of metal called a "grid". The purpose of these parts is to convert tiny fluctuations of current, coming into the set from the aerial, into powerful pulsations which will cause the loud-speaker to vibrate and so produce in it sounds corresponding to the electrical vibrations radiated from the broadcasting station.

The valve filament, the grid and the plate all have to be electrically connected to the various batteries and resistances in the receiver; there are, therefore, more lead-in wires than in a lamp. A lamp has only two; a valve may have as many as eight. Consequently the base of a valve is larger than the metal base of a lamp, and projecting split-pins are used instead of the flat

VALVE ELECTRODE ASSEMBLY

The types of valve in modern use have increased enormously during the past few years, not only for domestic radio, but also for service needs and for television. The assembly of valve electrodes is an operation calling for the utmost skill and delicate handling.

metal contacts. From the technical point of view these differences are, of course, immensely important; but as the stages of manufacture do not differ except in detail, the makers of lamps usually make valves also, and on machines which are almost exactly similar.

NEW LAMPS FOR OLD

The method of manufacture of electric lamps described above was, until recently, the last word in scientific efficiency and economical illumination, and it may be difficult to believe that, had the Second World War not intervened, this kind of lamp would already be out-of-date. But it is so. There is, in fact, no doubt whatever that in the

near future we shall all change over to a comparatively new method of electrical illumination which, both for domestic and industrial purposes, is as great an advance upon the present type of lamp as this was on the old-fashioned carbon filament bulb that preceded it.

This new kind of lighting is a miracle of scientific inventiveness. It is already being used extensively in war production plants, especially where night-shift work goes on, for the light it gives is so near to daylight that the difference can be detected only by delicate instruments. To the unaided eye it *is* daylight.

If you enter a room or workshop where this system has been installed, usually in the roof, or ceiling, you have the

COMPLEX MACHINES THAT MAKE LAMPS

The machines used in lamp-making are of extraordinary complexity and marvellous accuracy; in fine filaments they work to a limit of error of only a few millionths of an inch. This view of the machine erection shop of a lamp works shows some representative types.

impression that bright daylight from outside is streaming through a skylight. On closer inspection, you realise that what you thought was a skylight is an inverted trough containing a glass tube, which may be one, two or three feet in length, from which the "daylight" is streaming; but even then it is difficult to convince yourself that the illumination you see is artificial. Colours can be more easily distinguished by it and it is far easier on the eyes than any other kind of artificial light hitherto invented.

The name given to this new form of lighting is "fluorescent tube radiation". Not least of its merits is that it is so much more economical than ordinary electric lighting that one lamp of a given wattage will give at least two-and-a-half times as much light as an ordinary electric lamp of the same power.

The "bulb" (Fig. 6) is a glass tube which, for household use, will be ten inches to a foot in length and about two inches or less in diameter, having a brass fixing cap at each end. Just within each end of this glass tube, and connected to the brass cap at the same end, is a tiny coil of metal wire. The rest of the tube contains no filament but is filled with mercury vapour. The interior surface of the tube is coated with a thin layer of a chalk-like substance which is known by the name of "fluorescent medium".

FLUORESCENCE

Fluorescent substances have the almost miraculous power of converting "ultra-violet" light, which is invisible, into light like sunshine. When the current is passed into one of these new lamps the mercury vapour gives off a faint ultra-violet light which, as it passes through the fluorescent coating of the

EXHAUSTING THE CATHODE RAY TUBE

The cathode ray tube is one of the most versatile pieces of electrical apparatus ever developed. It is used for a wide variety of electrical measurements, for radio direction-finding, for television, etc. Some cathode ray tubes are used in a high vacuum state, and others of a different type are gas-filled, but whether vacuum or gas-filled, all cathode ray tubes have to be first evacuated completely of air. This intricate machine carries out the evacuation process.

tube, produces a brilliant but soft light with all the characteristics of daylight.

One astonishing thing about the new light is that it is almost cold. If you put your finger on an ordinary hundred-watt lamp bulb after it has been alight for a few minutes, the heat will burn you; but you could hold a lighted "fluorescent emission" lamp of the same illuminating power for hours on end. And the light is spread over so large an area of the glass surface that it produces far less glare than an ordinary electric lamp of similar power, where the light source is concentrated in a very much smaller space. Shadows are lost, too, for it spreads the light evenly over large areas instead of radiating it, as the ordinary lamp does, from a sharp-point focus.

People in the United States are already enjoying the benefits of this new lighting system, not only for domestic and industrial lighting but for many purposes of an entirely new kind. For example, it has been found that every different kind of microbe gives off a particular colour under this fluorescent illumination; a new weapon, therefore, has been put into the hands of research workers. Fungus diseases and other plant infections can be detected by their fluorescence when exposed to the mercury-vapour lamp.

The new lamps are simpler in structure than is the present type of electric bulb and the operations of manufacture are few. A length of glass tube is coated internally with the white fluorescent film. The tiny filaments are fitted at each end of the tube, which is then exhausted of air, filled with mercury vapour and sealed. Brass caps are fitted just in the same way as with ordinary lamps—and that is all.

One can safely predict that, within a very few years, these new lamps and the new kind of light they give will have superseded entirely the systems we are at present using; "cold light" will no longer be a scientist's dream, but the domestic possession of every householder throughout the civilised world.

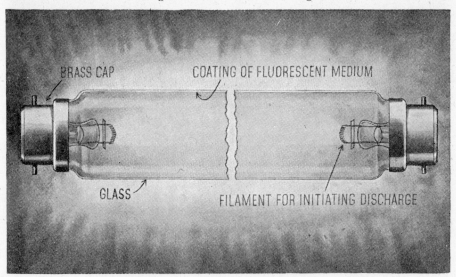

BRASS CAP   COATING OF FLUORESCENT MEDIUM

GLASS

FILAMENT FOR INITIATING DISCHARGE

SECTION OF FLUORESCENT DISCHARGE TUBE

Fig. 6. *Discharge tubes of this kind are used for the most up-to-date lighting installations. The tube is filled with mercury vapour; the filaments are seen at each end.*

FALSE TEETH

Moulding the Mouth. Base-Plates. The Articulator. Matching Nature's Handiwork. Fixing Teeth to Gums. The Flask. Vulcanising. Filing and Polishing. Metal and Plastic Dentures.

THE use of artificial teeth to replace natural teeth that have been lost or decayed is a very ancient practice. In1885 archeologists discovered the skull of a man belonging to the Etruscan civilisation (which flourished in Central Italy some five hundred years before Christ), with a set of animal's teeth firmly fixed in the jaws!

Until comparatively recent times, it was customary to replace the tops of decayed natural teeth with sound teeth from some other person's jaw—the "other person" probably being a corpse from which the teeth had been extracted after death! It is a far cry from crude methods such as these and the discomforts they must have involved, to the skilful and precisely accurate methods by which false teeth are made today. Anything from single teeth to complete sets can now be provided within a few hours, and they will fit so perfectly that, after getting accustomed to the "feel" of them, the wearers soon become completely unconscious of their presence.

MODELLING THE DENTURE

The first step in the manufacture of a denture is usually taken before the natural teeth are extracted. The dental surgeon takes a mould or pattern of the mouth, showing the shape and arrangement of the natural teeth, which is used as a model by the dental mechanic who constructs an artificial set as nearly as possible a precise replica of the original. This is not always done; partly because it adds to the expense, and partly because the patient may prefer to have a new set in which original blemishes have not been reproduced.

After the natural teeth have been extracted and the gums have been given time to heal and harden, the real job of preparing a set of false teeth begins with the making of an accurate model of the patient's jaw to which the false teeth will at a later stage be fitted.

DENTAL "COMPOSITION"

From the patient's point of view, this operation is a simple one. He is seated in the dental chair and told to open his mouth wide. The dentist then takes a shallow metal tray (Fig. 1A), rather like a horse-shoe, filled with a pliable substance called "composition" which, whilst warm, is soft and, therefore, moulds itself to the shape of anything against which it is pressed. This he inserts in the patient's mouth (Fig. 2 (1)) and presses gently over the gums and any natural teeth that may remain in them, until they are completely covered. He leaves it for a few moments to cool, perhaps spraying the tray with cold water, which hardens the composition and thus hastens the process.

Then, with the utmost care, tray and composition are lifted from the gums and removed from the mouth. The composition now bears an exact imprint, in reverse, of the patient's jaw; there is a deep hole the exact size and shape of every projecting tooth; there is a groove for every ridge of gum (Fig. 1c)

If the patient requires false teeth for both his upper and lower jaws, two such moulds are of course made, one for each

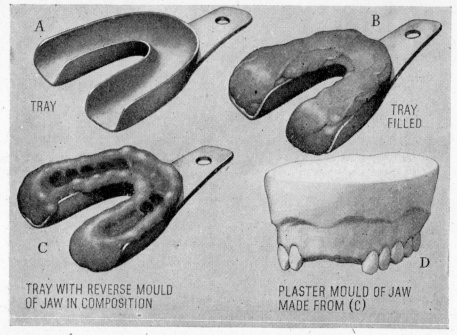

A — TRAY

B — TRAY FILLED

C — TRAY WITH REVERSE MOULD OF JAW IN COMPOSITION

D — PLASTER MOULD OF JAW MADE FROM (C)

FIRST STAGE IN MAKING A DENTURE

Fig. 1. *Here are seen* (A) *tray used to take the first impression;* (B) *the tray filled with "composition" and* (C) *imprint of the jaw.* (D) *shows the first mould made from* (C).

jaw. When these have set hard, they are sent to the dental mechanic, whose first task is to make plaster of paris moulds from each tray. He does this by pouring liquid plaster of paris into the hollowed-out composition (Fig. 2 (2)), so that when the plaster is set and the composition has been removed, he has a complete duplicate in plaster of the patient's mouth, showing all the remaining teeth in their exact position and reproducing with perfect fidelity every ridge and crevice of the mouth cavity (Fig. 1D).

The process has now reached a point at which the utmost skill and artistic ability of the dental mechanic are called into play. He has to model, in wax, a complete artificial "base-plate" (Fig. 2 (3)) for each jaw upon the plaster moulds and must take many factors into consideration. For the artificial gums must

be thick enough both to form a firm foundation for the teeth and to fill out the patient's cheeks sufficiently to restore the appearance he had before his teeth were removed; yet if they are too thick they will be unsightly and uncomfortable in wear, and if too thin they will not stand the pressure they have to bear. Again, they must be of such a height that when the mouth is closed the jaws will be just as far apart as they were with the natural teeth; and, when both upper and lower sets are being made, they must fit one into the other so that the jaws can open and close naturally without having to move sideways, forwards or backwards to enable the teeth to be brought together in a comfortable position.

It is said that it takes at least five years of training before a dental mechanic becomes competent at his job. When one realises that he must be an expert modeller in wax, as well as a craftsman in porcelain, gold, rubber and modern plastics, it is not difficult to realise why this should be so.

Before he sets about moulding his wax gums, or "bites" as they are called, the mechanic fixes the "articulator" (Fig. 3). This consists essentially of a strong brass or steel frame upon which the models can be mounted so that the upper and lower jaws are in the same relative positions as those of the patient. He then takes a quantity of soft, warm wax and moulds for each jaw a bite (Fig. 2 (4)). This is a complete gum, fitting the jaws exactly as the false teeth will fit them; there are no actual teeth in a bite but the wax is built up to the height the teeth will occupy.

FIRST FITTING

When the wax bites are ready and hardened they are sent to the dental surgeon, who fits them into the patient's mouth (Fig. 2 (5)) and makes any adjustments that may be necessary to ensure perfect comfort; taking off a little here, adding a little there, just as a tailor does when fitting a suit or costume. At the same time, if he has not done so already, the surgeon decides upon the size and colour of the teeth to be used in order to match the remaining natural teeth.

False teeth are made of a special kind of hard porcelain. How hard this is may be judged by the fact that the pressure of the bite of an adult male person of average strength is 150 lb. per square inch, while that of a woman's bite is usually about 125 lb. per square inch.

Every tooth is made separately. There are shapes corresponding to those of all the different kinds of teeth—incisors for the front of the mouth, canines or "dog teeth", bicuspids or premolars, and molars. Teeth vary enormously in

E.T.T.S.—C

colour, too. Some are white, some yellow and some grey or brown. It is important from the point of view of appearance that the artificial should closely match the natural teeth, especially at the front of the mouth; and there are dozens of different shades and colours made so that every variety of natural tooth can be duplicated.

When the dental surgeon has satisfied himself that the wax bite is a perfect fit, and has chosen the size and colour of the teeth for his patient's use, the wax bite, together with instructions about the teeth, is returned to the dental mechanic. The mechanic then prepares another set of wax gums, this time fitting into them the actual teeth (Fig. 2 (6)). Each one of these teeth must be filed and adjusted to interlock correctly with the teeth of the other jaw when both sets have been brought together in the correct position in the articulator.

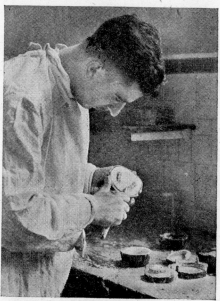

DENTAL MECHANIC AT WORK

The teeth are in position in the flask; the mechanic is giving the final touches to the plaster before melting away the wax gums.

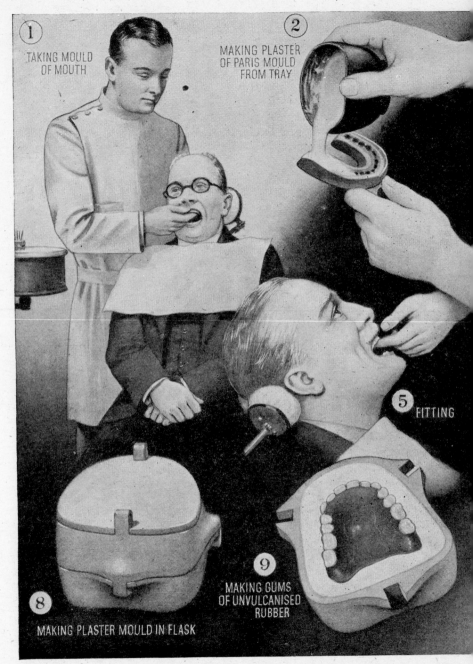

STAGES IN THE MAKING

Fig. 2. *Dentistry today inflicts no pain or anxiety on the patient. (1) The first mould being taken. (2) Making the plaster mould. (3) Wax on which the gum is modelled. (4) The "bite"*

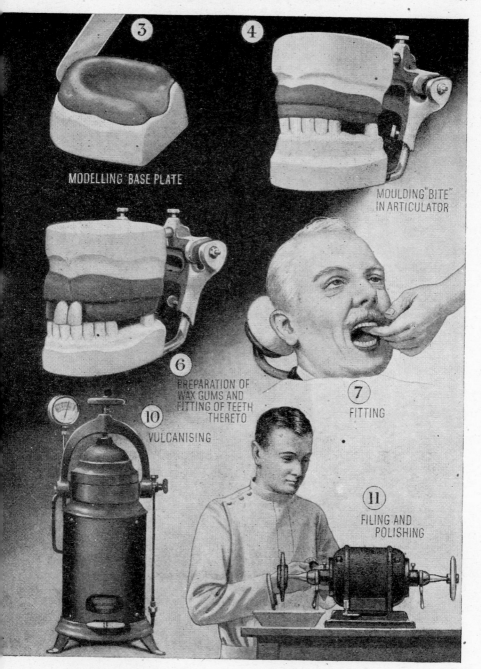

OF AN ARTIFICIAL DENTURE

being moulded and (5) the first fitting. (6) The teeth embedded in a second set of gums and (7) These being fitted. (8), (9), (10) How the actual set is made. (11) The final polishing.

The teeth are fixed as follows: each tooth has, projecting from it at right angles to the surface on the inner side, one or more gold or platinum "tags" or "pins" which are embedded in the surface of the wax gums by pressure (Fig. 4). The wax gums are not strong enough to hold the pins very firmly, but this does not matter because, as we shall see presently, the gums of the teeth the patient will actually wear are made, not of this wax, but of vulcanite or some other substance. The wax is employed for fitting purposes only.

SECOND FITTING

Having then made the new waxen set of gums into which he has fitted porcelain teeth, the dental mechanic rests from his labours whilst the dental surgeon gives the patient another fitting and notes any final adjustments that need to be made (Fig. 2 (7)). Then the waxen set returns to the dental mechanic.

Let us remind ourselves of the stage that has now been reached.

The mechanic has a complete set of artificial teeth that fits the patient perfectly. The actual teeth are those the patient will in due course use; but the gums into which they have been fitted are made of soft wax, useless for wear, as it is comparatively soft and brittle. It is now, therefore, necessary to replace the waxen gums with gums made of vulcanised rubber but without altering by a fraction of an inch either the position of the teeth in relation to each other or the shape of the artificial gum.

FLASK AND LID

This is a most delicate and difficult operation; and it is performed as follows. The mechanic has an appliance known as a "flask" (Figs. 2 (8), 5). This resembles a box, built of heavy brass to withstand great pressure; it is made in two halves which fit accurately together, the "lid" half being almost as deep inside as the base. When, therefore, the two halves are taken apart, each has the appearance of a deep tray, about six inches square and three inches in height.

Into one of these trays fluid plaster of paris is poured and, before it has had time to harden, the gums and teeth are placed in it so that the under surface of the wax gums and all the teeth are embedded in the plaster. The plaster is then allowed to set.

Next, a fine fabric is laid over the surface of the plaster and the exposed upper surface of the wax denture. The "lid" half of the brass flask is filled with plaster and the two halves of the flask brought together, so that when the plaster has again hardened there is a mould of the upper part of the denture in the "lid" half of the flask, which can be separated from the other half because the fabric has prevented the two parts from sticking together.

REMOVING THE WAX

The part of the flask containing the wax denture is now heated so that the wax melts and can be poured away. This operation leaves all the porcelain teeth firmly embedded in the solid plaster and surrounded by a hollow space which is the exact shape of the gums. This space is now carefully packed with unvulcanised rubber of the same colour as the patient's gums (Fig. 2 (9)). This, being soft and pliable in texture, can be moulded in the fingers almost like plasticine. The mechanic presses it carefully into position, taking care to fill all hollows and interstices in the mould. Having done this, he takes the "lid" portion of his flask and places it on the base half so that the plaster impression which it contains of the upper surface of the denture is pressing on to the rubber. The set of teeth is now ready for vulcanising.

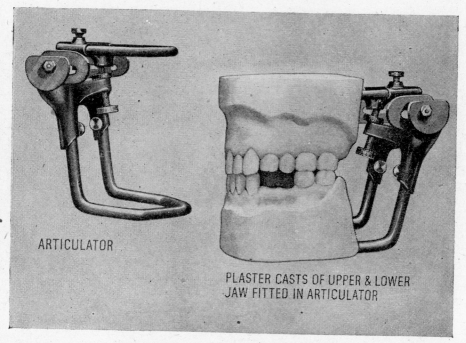

ARTICULATOR

PLASTER CASTS OF UPPER & LOWER
JAW FITTED IN ARTICULATOR

THE "BITE" IS ADJUSTED ACCURATELY

Fig. 3. *It is of the utmost importance that the "bite" should be critically accurate. To insure this an articulator (left) is employed and is here (right) shown in use.*

Vulcanising is a process by which indiarubber is hardened under pressure by steam. The dental mechanic's vulcanising plant (Figs. 2 (10), 5) is an appliance that works on the same principle as the "pressure cookers" that many housewives nowadays use in their kitchens; indeed, the work could be done in one of these cookers, though the actual appliance used is better adapted to the job. It consists, usually, of a metal cylinder standing on a gas ring. The bottom end of the cylinder contains water; above it is a perforated shelf to accommodate the "flask" containing the denture which is to be vulcanised, and at the top there is a heavy lid which, when closed, can be clamped down. The cylinder is fitted with a pressure gauge.

When the flask containing the unvulcanised teeth has been prepared in the manner we have described, the gas ring in the vulcaniser is lighted and the water heated. Then the flask is put on its shelf and the lid is clamped down, so that as the water comes to the boil the steam pressure gets higher until it reaches 150 lb. to the square inch.

This heavy pressure on the two halves of the flask presses them tightly together and, by doing so, forces the rubber into every nook and cranny of the mould—wherever the original wax was—until it is a perfect duplicate of the wax denture, with the porcelain teeth firmly fixed by their metal tags and gripped by the rubber that surrounds them on three sides.

After pressure has been maintained for an hour the steam is released, the vulcaniser is allowed to cool and the brass box is opened. Gentle tapping and scraping breaks up the plaster of paris, leaving the complete set of teeth strong, firm and almost ready for the patient.

A little more work still needs to be done on them, however. Tiny shreds of rubber cling here and there; a few sharp corners need to be filed down, and some polishing is required (Fig. 2 (11)). Then they return to the dental surgeon, who gives the patient his final fitting and makes whatever minor adjustments may be required before the wearer goes home to have a shot at eating his first solid meal with his new teeth.

Denture plates are not invariably made of vulcanised rubber; indeed with the invention of resinous plastics, it is

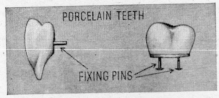

PORCELAIN TEETH

FIXING PINS

FIXING THE TEETH

Fig. 4. *Porcelain teeth, fitted with pins, are embedded in the vulcanite or metal gums. The pins may be attached either at the side or root of the tooth, according to its shape and the position it holds in the denture.*

probable that rubber will soon be considered "old-fashioned" in dental practice. Plates made of metal—usually gold—have been made for many years.

Plastic resin is as strong as vulcanised rubber and simpler to mould. It requires no vulcanising. The process of making artificial teeth with it follows the same procedure as with rubber, up to the point at which the flask comes into use. Then powdered resin is mixed with a special liquid to the consistency of stiff paste, and this is forced into the plaster of paris mould instead of the unvulcanised rubber. The flask is closed in the ordinary way, but instead of being heated under pressure it is boiled for a period, when the resin "sets" and hardens as rubber does when vulcanised.

When denture plates are made of metal, the process differs from that described above, from the point where the plaster moulds are made.

For metal dentures these two moulds, one of the upper surface of the set of teeth and the other of the lower, are cast in metal. A sheet of gold of the required size for the dental plate is then heated and, when soft, pressed or hammered into shape between these two metal matrices. The process of heating and pressing, which calls for most patient and accurate workmanship, may have to be repeated a number of times before the gold is formed into the exact shape of the moulds.

FIXING TEETH TO PLATE

When a metal plate has been prepared in this way the teeth have to be welded or riveted to it; in some cases, they may be fitted into a strip of vulcanised rubber which, in its turn, is riveted to the gold plate. The procedure varies according to the number of teeth to be fitted and their position in the mouth; but is always difficult and delicate.

The manufacture of artificial dentures is one of the few modern crafts that will never be replaced by mass-production methods of manufacture. False teeth must be individually made from start to finish; and to construct them with the accuracy of fit necessary to ensure comfort, the dental mechanic must be meticulously accurate and careful over every detail of his work. He must, in fact, be an artist as well as a craftsman. How well he does his job is attested by the fact that of all those who nowadays wear false teeth, seven out of ten prefer them to those they have lost. That may be, in part, because their natural teeth were none too good—nevertheless it is a very high tribute.

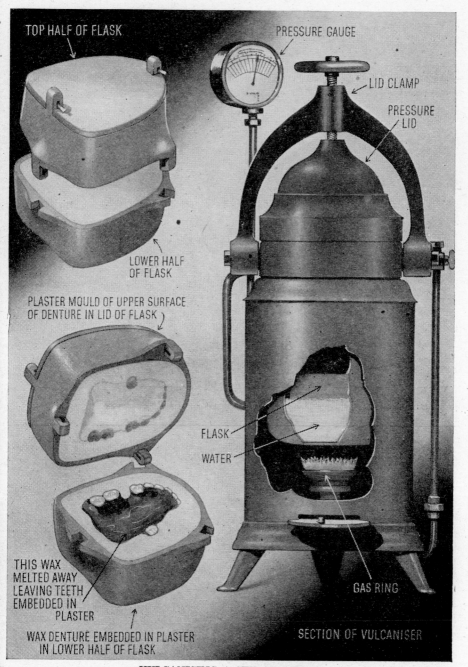

TOP HALF OF FLASK

PRESSURE GAUGE

LID CLAMP

PRESSURE LID

LOWER HALF OF FLASK

PLASTER MOULD OF UPPER SURFACE OF DENTURE IN LID OF FLASK

FLASK

WATER

THIS WAX MELTED AWAY LEAVING TEETH EMBEDDED IN PLASTER

WAX DENTURE EMBEDDED IN PLASTER IN LOWER HALF OF FLASK

GAS RING

SECTION OF VULCANISER

VULCANISING A SET OF TEETH

Fig. 5. *The flask (top and bottom left) in which the teeth are transferred from wax to vulcanised rubber and (right) the vulcanising plant in which this is hardened.*

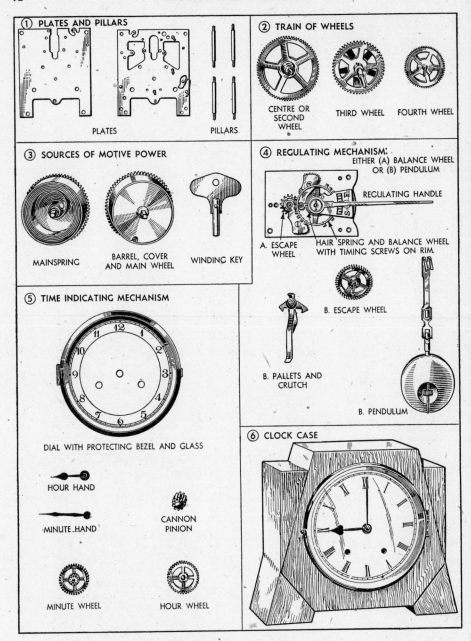

THE SIX CHIEF PARTS OF A CLOCK

Fig. 1. *The main components of a clock are: (1) Brass plates, which, when connected by the pillars, make the framework; (2) Train of wheels to communicate movement to the hands; (3) Mainspring and barrel; (4) Regulating mechanism to control speed of the motive power; (5) Dial and hands, with the wheels that move them; (6) Case.*

CLOCKS AND WATCHES

Parts of a Clock. Design and Materials. Stamping Machines. Cutting the Wheels. Assembly. Casemaking. Making a Watch. Synthetic Jewels. The Train of Wheels. Springs and Balances. Testing and Timing.

THE making of clocks and watches follows similar lines, since both require (Fig. 1) six similar elements in their construction. There are (1) the two plates within which the movement is contained. In a clock these are called *front and back plates,* and in a watch *top and bottom plates,* that being their position when the movement dial is uppermost.

Between the framework of these two plates, with their connecting *pillars,* is to be found the mechanism, consisting of (2) the *train* of wheels by which movement is communicated to the hands: and (3) the source of motive power, generally a steel *mainspring* in its *barrel* or case. True, there is also another type of clock in which the motive power may be a *weight,* but we are here considering mainly those clocks used to show the time in thousands of homes: the spring-driven, wood-cased mantelpiece clock, turned out by the factories in large quantities.

At some point between the wheels and the mainspring there must be (4) a regulating mechanism, to control the speed at which the motive power is allowed to operate the wheels. The devising and perfecting of this mechanism, which is the heart of the clock or

MACHINES THAT "EAT UP" METAL RODS
The supplies of metal rod seen in the stands will be fed to the machines to become small toothed wheels or pinions, hour and minute hands, and other clock parts.

watch, has kept inventors busy during the 600 years for which clocks have been known. It takes the form of an *escape wheel*, having projections that allow of a momentary stoppage of the drive from the mainspring. How long the stoppage is to last is determined by the swinging of the *balance wheel* (alternatively by the pendulum in larger clocks), this providing a ticking action.

Up to this point we have a mechanism that turns at a very precisely controlled speed, and to make it into a clock or watch there is needed (5) an *indicator*, consisting of dial and hands.

To enclose the whole is the purpose of (6) the *case*, in which the movement, as the clock- or watchmaker calls it, is protected and also rendered portable.

This mechanical conception of a timepiece and its task must be kept in mind

if we are to understand rightly what goes to the making of such time indicators. To us, an hour represents so much time, a portion of the day in which to do things, but to the clock the "hour" represents nothing more than a measured distance which has to be travelled, or, in the language of mechanics, the number of teeth of a particular wheel that have to pass a certain point in regular movement.

Before beginning to describe the modern processes of clock and watch manufacture, a short digression will serve to show to what aim the clockmaker's energies are directed. The distinction made above, between the passing of time and the mechanism that registers its own number of turns as it goes along, represents two things that actually have nothing whatsoever in

WHERE THE CLOCKS TAKE SHAPE

Fig. 2. *Seated at the conveyor belt are men and women each of whom fits a part in its appointed place. On reaching the end of the belt the clock, minus its case, is going. On the centre table lie cases awaiting filling, and cased clocks ready for timing tests.*

common. It is our minds that translate the movement into "time". The achievement to which the clockmaker sets himself will be better understood if we view a clock thus. Suppose we happen to pass a machine one day, at exact noon, and mark with chalk the tooth in a particular wheel that is uppermost at that moment. Between that moment and the next day's noon lie thousands of revolutions, and yet on approaching the machine a second time, twenty-four hours later, we find that same tooth again uppermost. This is in fact what happens with the clock. The minute hand of a clock represents that chalked tooth.

Labels on figure: STRIKING TRAIN THIS SIDE · ESCAPE WHEEL · TIME TRAIN THIS SIDE · PALLETS · PILLARS · PENDULUM BRACKET · PLATES · SUSPENSION SPRING WITH PENDULUM BELOW · STRIKING RACK HOOK · GATHERING PALLET · STRIKING RACK · HAMMER TAIL ARBOR · STEPPED SNAIL · SECOND WHEEL & PINION · MINUTE WHEEL · HANDS ATTACHED HERE · HOUR WHEEL · TIME MAINSPRING BARREL · MAINSPRING BARREL · RATCHET & SQUARE FOR WINDING TIME · GREAT WHEEL · RATCHET & SQUARE FOR WINDING STRIKE

A COMPLETED MOVEMENT

Fig. 3. *The clock as it leaves the conveyor belt, showing the mainspring barrel and great wheel, with the second wheel above it. The movement shown is a "strike", hence the second mainspring and (centre) "snail" to control the number of hammer blows for the hour.*

To enter a clock factory is to realise that clock manufacture is a highly specialised branch of engineering, governed by blue prints at every stage. These engineer's drawings emanate from the drawing office, where much thought is given by the technicians to the features a new clock model is to possess.

Broadly speaking, the method followed in clock production is not to produce the goods clock by clock, but rather to set the plant to make a large stock of each individual part, hundreds or thousands of them. For this purpose the raw material, in the form of sheets and rods of brass and steel, is sent out from the stores into the machine depart-

ments and converted by the plant into wheels, plates, spindles, small parts of diverse shapes, amounting perhaps to some 200 different kinds in all. By degrees these parts accumulate in the finished stores department in a collection of bins or box shelving, or in glass jars when the parts are very small, until enough of every part is available to make it worth while starting on the assembly of complete clocks.

The technicians of the drawing office, today's successors to the old-time clockmakers, specify what gauge, or thickness, of brass sheet is to be used, what diameter of brass or steel rod. These two metals, brass and steel, are

`A BATTERY OF STAMPING PRESSES

Fig. 4. *These stamping presses are fed with sheets and rods of brass which are pressed between hard steel dies, thus cutting blanks for wheels, levers, bridges, fixing brackets and other parts. The rods and strips with which they are fed are positioned by rollers.*

the chief materials that go to the making of a clock movement. A glance into the raw material stores of the factory will show the brass in two forms: (*a*) in sheets of considerable length but already cut to narrow widths of so many inches: (*b*) in rod form, in a range of diameters of specified fractions of an inch. From the brass strip will be made the plates that constitute the framework, the wheels, the mainspring barrel, and the dial. From the steel rods come the arbors or slender shafts on which the wheels are mounted; the smaller toothed wheels, called pinions when they have only a few teeth, say up to twelve in number; the hands; perhaps also the pillars, unless brass is preferred.

The plant in a clock factory will consist of automatic or semi-automatic machines, working mainly on the principle of the turret lathe, with its revolving capstan of various tools. They are indeed equipped with a number of tools that come into action by operation of the machine itself. The complete cycle of operations will produce one part, on completion of which the machine may stop until an attendant restarts it with fresh material for a repetition of the process. Such a machine would be called a semi-automatic. A fully automatic one will go on repeating its cycle of operations, the completed parts dropping into some receptacle until by degrees the machine, having "eaten up" its length of brass or steel rod, stops automatically.

This section of a clock factory is impressive because of its high mechanical ingenuity, but it is not spectacular in the sense that you see a clock actually

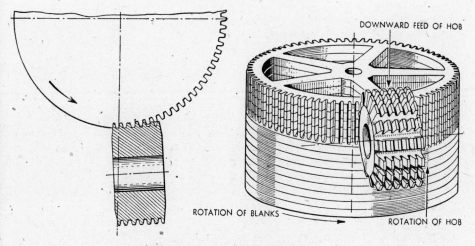

DOWNWARD FEED OF HOB

ROTATION OF BLANKS

ROTATION OF HOB

MAKING TOOTHED WHEELS—1

Fig. 5. *In one method, that illustrated above, a hobbing cutter "generates" the toothed wheels as its steel teeth work their way down a stack of blanks, these meanwhile rotating slowly so that the likewise rotating cutter can shape the teeth all round their edges.*

taking shape. Far from it: you may stand before some of these automatics and still not appreciate what is happening, until the engineer in charge lets you into the secret. He will put his fingers into a receptacle swimming with oil and extract therefrom one of the spindles that keep dropping into it as that machine's contribution towards the finished timekeeper.

What you do notice is that each machine is fed with a many-foot-long bar or rod of metal that is gradually getting shorter.

Having thus given a general impression of the machine shops, we can study the manufacture in detail. Of the six main components into which we divided a clock there came first the brass

plates that hold the movement together. To make these, powerful stamping presses (Fig. 4) are fed continuously with the brass sheet, and at each descent of the stamping head a blank is cut out, on the same principle that the Mint stamps out pennies from a long band of brass. Whilst the press provides the power to cut through the stout brass

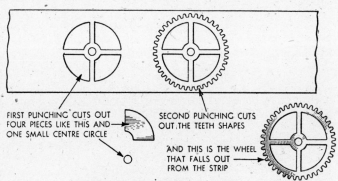

FIRST PUNCHING CUTS OUT FOUR PIECES LIKE THIS AND ONE SMALL CENTRE CIRCLE

SECOND PUNCHING CUTS OUT THE TEETH SHAPES

AND THIS IS THE WHEEL THAT FALLS OUT FROM THE STRIP

MAKING TOOTHED WHEELS—2

Fig. 6. *A second method frequently employed is the use of a die which stamps four pieces out of a long strip of brass to form the arms, and a small circular piece for the centre. A second die marks out the shape of the toothed circle, and when this is pressed out from the strip the result is a complete wheel.*

sheet, perhaps an eighth of an inch in thickness, hard steel dies decide the actual shape of the blank.

The blank, whether it be for front or back plate, will at the first operation receive only its shape in outline. A second stamping press will then cut out portions of the plate where metal can be spared, since it is not required to hold anything at that point, so economising in the use of metal and avoiding undue weight. A third operation is that by which an accurate press tool makes the holes in each plate to act as bearings for each separate spindle of the wheels. These holes must be accurate in their distances apart and also in their individual diameters, or smooth working of the gears will not be attained. It is most important that the blanks be correctly positioned each time before the press descends. Finally, the plates will also need holes drilled to receive the stout brass or steel pillars that bind them into a framework.

Wheel blanks and other clock parts made from sheet metal are produced by similar stamping presses. The larger wheels are not solid disks, like the smaller ones, but show a cross of four arms. It is this that is produced first by the stamping press; that is, four quarter-circle open spaces are punched out under the first press head, along with the central hole by which the wheel is afterwards mounted on its arbor or spindle (Fig. 6). The brass band moves on under the second press head, and while head No. 1 is cutting out another cross, No. 2 stamps out the wheel outline. The blanks are now free from the brass sheet as loose disks. A small but

INSPECTING THE FINISHED CLOCKS

Fig. 7. *The completed clocks are subject to a daily check against the standard clock seen in the background. Close inspection of the illustration will show some variation between the minute hands. A variation of more than a few seconds per day from the master clock means that they must return to the factory for adjustment, and a further timing test.*

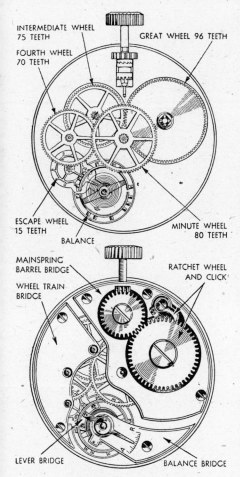

INTERMEDIATE WHEEL
75 TEETH

GREAT WHEEL 96 TEETH

FOURTH WHEEL
70 TEETH

ESCAPE WHEEL
15 TEETH

BALANCE

MINUTE WHEEL
80 TEETH

MAINSPRING
BARREL BRIDGE

RATCHET WHEEL
AND CLICK

WHEEL TRAIN
BRIDGE

LEVER BRIDGE

BALANCE BRIDGE

A WATCH MOVEMENT

Fig. 8. *Shown above are the main working parts of a watch as they appear when assembled in their places and in going order.*

important point to notice here is the way the operator registers the blank under head No. 2 by using the central hole, punched under head No. 1, to fit over a round-headed positioning stud. Unless something like this were done there would be no guarantee that the central hole and outer circular shape were in concentric positions.

The wheel blanks still require their teeth to be cut, and here it is that com-

plete discarding of the old method of cutting each tooth individually proved necessary if clocks were to be produced at popular prices. The modern method is to use hobbing machines in which not one, but a stack of wheel blanks is pressed together and centred on the machine so that the whole can revolve as a single column (Fig. 5). The tooth cutter on the machine then proceeds to "nibble" its way down the row of blanks, cutting out the form of the teeth as it proceeds. In due course the round is completed, and when the wheel disks are released from the machine one may find thirty or forty wheels, all alike and cut with teeth of the right shape and depth. This shaping of the teeth is very important, and in higher grade clocks each wheel, after having been mounted on its own arbor, is carefully gone over once again with a trueing cutter to remove any remaining roughnesses.

ARBOR AND PINION

The arbor just mentioned is the steel rod on which each wheel is set, and it is turned down to shape from the lengths of round steel that came from the stores. On some completed arbors it will be noticed that there is not only the wheel, but that part of the thickness of the arbor has been made into a second smaller toothed wheel, called a pinion. The rod has therefore to be turned down in the automatic lathe to different thicknesses, which themselves will extend to specific distances along its length. All this is ingeniously carried out by the various cutting tools, brought down to bear on the revolving rod in their proper sequence. Such matters as the depth of cut and the width of each variation or change in thickness along the arbor's length are governed by stops, and it is the business of the engineer in charge to set these, and see that nothing becomes changed by vibration

WORKING DRAWINGS OF A WATCH

Fig. 9. *Detailed plans giving exact measurements are made by draughtsmen before a watch goes into production. Several hundred drawings may be needed for a single part.*

requisite strength being nicely adjusted by the tempering, width, thickness and length of the spring. Too strong a spring merely causes unnecessary wear of the gears. Making the barrel, in which the spring lies coiled, requires the heavier type of stamping press, since the whole shape, rather like a pill-box with an added wheel underneath, is pressed out at one operation from the brass ingot. The rest is lathe work: turning the face true, the periphery where later the teeth are cut, the inside and the outside of the "pill-box".. Pressing a tongue into the roundness of the wall makes a hook on which to fasten one end of the mainspring. The other end is attached to the arbor, whose squared end receives the key by which the clock is wound.

Dials are made from brass plate, with the figures etched in and blacked over, the remaining surface being silvered. Hands are of steel, and are stamped.

The part in a clock factory that the general visitor finds attractive is the assembling department. This is planned on the moving belt principle (Fig. 2), girls sitting alongside. The supply of parts which each is to fit in comes to her in trays arriving along the moving belt. Into the plate holes are inserted the wheel arbors, nuts are screwed on to the pillar ends, and the clock begins to take shape (Fig. 3). In the later stages men sit at the belt, or at a separate bench, carrying out the more skilful tasks.

or the entry of foreign matter during the day. He must also maintain the sharpness of the cutting tools and see that a fresh length of metal rod is fed into the machine whenever the length in actual use is exhausted.

It is part of the automatic operation to cut off the finished arbor from the main rod at the moment of completion, but the arbor may still need a further operation if there are pinion teeth yet to cut. A second machine undertakes this, each arbor being set individually between centres and the form of the teeth milled out. A counting wheel, co-axial with the arbor, moves it round by ratchet as each groove is cut. Another wheel counts the teeth as they are cut, and stops the machine after the last tooth—a neat example of the machine that "does its own thinking".

Blued steel springs come to the clock factory from specialist firms, the

The completed movements, often without a case, are set going and put on to racks where each face can be clearly seen (Fig. 7). The purpose is to test the individual timekeeping, and as one clock or another is found to be going fast or slow the timer makes the necessary adjustment.

Much of the attractiveness of a clock depends on the casemaker's art. This is a separate branch of the industry, allied in its methods to the cabinet-making and furniture-making crafts. Woods selected for colour and grain, and moulded ornaments are often used. According to the shape of the dial—whether round, square or fancy—the chromium-plated brass bezel that frames the dial follows suit. Being hinged it opens to give access to the winding holes.

Producing a watch involves similar but more intricate processes. When the back of the watch is opened (Fig. 8) one sees the same framework of two plates, with the movement secured between them. But in place of the full-width plate found on the clock, one of the plates is seen to be subdivided into a number of smaller plates. True, the very simplest type of watch has but one back plate, hiding from view most of the movement; but the better watch uses several bridges, as they are called, and through the gaps the movement can be seen working.

As in the clock, motive power is generated in the coils of the mainspring and travels through the train of gear wheels to the hands. The mainspring would entirely unwind itself in a fraction of a minute unless there were a means of checking it and causing the power to be released in small doses, as it were. This function is exercised by the little balance wheel, whose to-and-fro motion is well known to everyone.

Automatic machines are the rule in watch factories; in some of the very largest there may be as many as two

WATCHES BY MASS PRODUCTION

A modern watch factory is largely automatic. These machines, which form the minute wheels, pinions and springs, operate unattended until their supply of metal gives out.

thousand such machines. With this equipment it is not surprising that up to 4,000 watches are produced per day.

Every detail—the length of the tiniest screw, diameter of a jewel hole and width of the pivot that is to turn in it, and exactly how much play there is to be allowed between them—is calculated in thousandths of a millimetre in the drawing office (Fig. 9). Here, draughtsmen, standing before large easels, prepare drawings for the plates already mentioned, naturally on a much larger scale, as though the watch were two feet wide.

DESIGNING WATCH PARTS

In the same way they proceed with drawings for each of the small parts whose total of some 200 constitutes the complete watch. Each of the 1,000 operations required to produce these parts has also to be governed by blue prints, so that every department is furnished with complete guidance. Each foreman in charge of a machine group knows then that all his output will have to meet those measurements, and it will, in fact, be tested in every dimension and at several stages of manufacture.

Here lies the secret of manufacturing watches at such a price that everyone can buy them: having automatic plant that can be set to work at very fine limits, and then gauging all finished products, often with maximum and minimum gauges. Contrast this with the method when watches were made by hand, each wheel being adapted to fit those it geared with in that particular watch, but perhaps useless for another watch.

The same procedure as that in clock factories is followed for watches: metal bars or strips, of brass and steel, up to ten feet long, are fed into the machines, where a succession of tools each contributes its part in reducing or otherwise shaping the material, after which it is

cut off the stock. This holds good for parts that can be worked into shape from round material, but many watch parts require stamping out from sheet by means of dies. The making of the hardened steel dies is a fine art in the watch industry, and microscopic accuracy is required in the measurements. A microscope is a familiar object in watch factories, since it is used for measuring as well as examining.

Coming to the parts in detail; the top plate, behind the dial, is cut out of strip brass by a series of presses on lines common to precision engineering practice. But then the plate is subjected to a further series of operations peculiar to watchmaking and necessitated by the desire to keep watches down to a reasonable thickness. This is the milling out or recessing of spaces in the brass plate to make room for the mainspring barrel

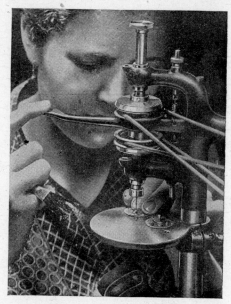

SKILL AND ACCURACY
This girl is tapping screw threads in the plates. One belt provides for the downward action, another withdraws the "tap". as the thread-making tool is called.

and some of the wheels. Milling cutters guided by cams make the curves and cut the circular recesses to the right depth. The plate needs also to be drilled with very fine holes where the pivots of the wheels are to be inserted. Correct spacing to a high degree of accuracy is essential here, otherwise when the wheels are inserted later the teeth may engage too tightly and bind, or too loosely and slip, with a risk of breakage. That is why so many operations, such as drilling holes or cutting teeth, are done twice over in watch practice, once to create the shape and again, with a finer tool, to render the shape or hole true to the ten-thousandth of an inch.

Pressed by delicate machines into some of the plate and bridge holes are the jewels, used because they are harder than brass and can better withstand the friction of the turning pivots, which, being made of steel, might wear elongated holes in the brass and upset the correct meshing of the tiny teeth.

WATCH JEWELS

These jewels are a cause of some misunderstanding among the public who think of them as real rubies like those used for ornament. The modern watch is fitted with synthetic rubies, which are chemically the same and possess the same desirable quality of hardness, but cost only a small fraction by comparison, being a factory product. Their quality of smoothness is valuable in reducing friction, the more when you consider that the balance wheel must make 18,000 swings an hour, not much under *half a million* per day.

The method of making the train of wheels is not unlike that employed in the clock factories, though the delicacy of the operation can be imagined when teeth hardly to be seen have to be cut. Twenty or thirty wheels are cut in a batch. But the watchmaker's pride is a

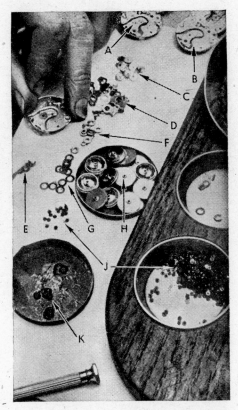

ASSEMBLING A WATCH

(A) *Movement without, and* (B) *with, rocking bar;* (C) *minute wheels;* (D) *rocking bars;* (E) *rocking bar with 3 wheels;* (F) *collets for middle wheels;* (G) *middle wheels of bar;* (H) *mainsprings in barrel;* (J) *screws for middle wheels;* (K) *end wheels of rocking bar.*

batch of escape wheels, with their peculiarly bent and "hooked" teeth. The little column of thirty blanks is attacked by seven milling cutters in turn, mounted round a drum, and each completing what it has to do fifteen times, for that number of teeth. In a watch this wheel is generally among the visible ones, glistening because it is made of steel, and not brass. The anchor-shaped lever you also know is produced from steel by similar shaping processes. It carries the two pallet stones whose

AN IMPORTANT TEST
Testing a hairspring for speed of vibration.
If it proves necessary it will be corrected.

red flash comes and goes—red, because they are made of synthetic ruby like the jewels, and flashing because they alternately stop and release the motion of the entire train, 18,000 times an hour.

The fine spiral hairspring (so called because in early watches it was an actual hair) and the mainspring, are supplied to the watch factory by specialist firms. So are the hands and dials, the silvered brass of the latter receiving the numerals by impression from a soft rubber pad which itself received the image from an inked engraved plate.

PARTS ON MOVING BELTS

The assembling rooms are free from the noise of machinery and kept scrupulously free from dust. The workers sit at long benches by good window light. Since the parts to be assembled are small and a small trayful lasts a long time, the moving belt principle is applied although, as the watch "grows" by passage from worker to worker, no belt is required. The familiar watchmaker's eyeglass, held in position by the muscles, is worn by every worker, since the parts to be handled are so small.

The balance wheels that at this stage are inserted by watchmakers are not toothed, as might be thought; the little

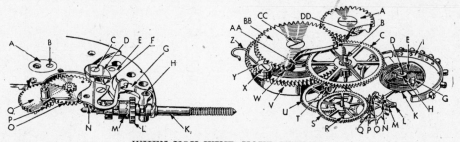

WHEN YOU WIND YOUR WATCH

All this mechanism comes into action—(Left) (A) Endpiece; (B) Lower endpiece screw; (C) Intermediate wheel bridge screw; (D) Intermediate wheel bridge; (E) Yoke; (F) Yoke spring; (G) Setting lever; (H) Setting lever screw; (K) Winding stem; (L) Winding pinion; (M) Clutch; (N) Intermediate wheel; (O) Minute wheel; (P) Cannon pinion; (Q) Hour wheel; (Right) (AA) Barrel-arbor; (BB) Ratchet wheel; (CC) Ratchet wheel screw; (DD) Crown wheel collet; (A) Crown wheel; (B) Centre wheel pinion; (C) Centre wheel; (D) Balance staff; (E) Balance spring; (F) Balance; (G) Stud; (H) Hairspring collet; (K) Roller; (L) Fork; (M) Exit pallet stone; (N) Pallet staff; (O) Entry pallet stone; (P) Escape wheel; (Q) Escape wheel pinion; (R) Fourth wheel pinion; (S) Fourth wheel; (T) Third wheel pinion; (U) Third wheel; (V) Mainspring barrel; (W) Mainspring; (X) Click screws; (Y) Click; (Z) Click spring.

THE FINAL INSPECTION

Fig. 10. *Finished watches undergo a timing test. It will be noticed that some of those shown have lost a few minutes; they will therefore receive further regulation before sale.*

projections seen on the outside are the regulating screws. Their delicate adjustment is skilled work, their making has involved many processes, and they have fulfilled their mission when, in the subsequent watch tests, the watch is found to keep good time irrespective of its position. Timing in different positions is needful, for on the wrist or in the pocket a watch is turned now this way, now that, but its rate must remain constant. Naturally, a good movement alone is capable of this fine adjustment, and the "timers" are men of great experience whose ambition it is to get high marks for their watches when the official tests are made (Fig. 10).

All self-respecting watches go forth with the name of their maker somewhere on the movement, though it may not always be on the dial. Such names or marks can be inscribed by a hard steel die stamping the letters into the brass or, in high-quality watches, be mechanically engraved on each movement. A very fine rotating cutter does the engraving, tracing the required letters under guidance of a pantograph system, of which it forms one point. At the other end of the pantograph, as these reducing or enlarging arms are called, is the pointer guided by the operator along the channels of the master letters, cut in a brass plate on a large scale, each letter perhaps one inch high.

So signed, the watch can embark on its life of never resting usefulness, which may well endure for many years.

A MONSTER ROLL OF STAMPS

Fig. 1. *After the paper has been gummed and the gum fractured, the surface smoothed and the long rolls split to a smaller size, the actual printing of the stamps is performed on rotary presses, the machine minder keeping constant watch for imperfections.*

POSTAGE STAMPS

£250 million worth of Stamps. Paper and Watermarks. Counting and Perforating. Gumming and Fracturing. Designs. Printing Methods. Surface Printing. Photogravure. Checking. What "Controls" are.

THE printing, control and sale of postage stamps involves a great deal of work of an intricate and detailed nature. The work in Britain comes under the Post Office, and some idea of the task involved may be gathered from the fact that the stamp store at Somerset House must hold adequate stocks of no fewer than 500 different kinds of stamps, as well as 50 kinds of stamped stationery. In the course of a year there are issued over 7,500,000,000 stamps in sheets or rolls; 28,500,000 in books; and 72,000,000 stamped envelopes and postcards. The total face value of these exceeds £250,000,000. With certain exceptions— such as stamps for fiscal purposes, pensions, unemployment, insurance, and entertainment duty—the Post Office Stores Department is responsible for every stage in the supply of this truly enormous and varied stock.

PRINTING CONTRACTS

The Post Office does not undertake the actual printing of stamps. This is done entirely by outside firms, although officers from the Stores Department are in control of the manufacture throughout all the stages. Great care is taken to ensure that only authorised printings are made, and no stamps may be printed by any firm except under a written warrant. Current stamps are printed under a ten-year contract. The necessary paper, and also the plates or printing cylinders themselves, are kept in the custody of the Post Office representatives at the works, and are issued when the actual printing begins. Checks are imposed at every stage.

The paper for the stamps is made at a separate mill, the contract for the supply being arranged by the Stores Department of the Post Office. The work is closely supervised by an officer from the Stores Department who is stationed at the paper mill. He has in his custody the "dandy rolls" which are used for producing the watermark; these are the property of the Post Office.

WATERMARK AND DANDY ROLL

The watermark is a device impressed in the paper. In the case of British stamps it consists of the royal cypher, the letters GR and a crown; for stamps of the colonies the initials are CA ("Crown Agents") and a crown, and various appropriate designs are used by other countries. The dandy-roll by which the watermark is impressed in the paper is a cylinder of wire gauze carrying a number of watermark devices punched out of sheet brass by means of steel dies. These brass devices are sewn on to the gauze with brass wire in the required places. The cylinder is passed over the pulp whilst it is still damp, and it compresses the paper where it touches, leaving on it the imprint of the design.

When the paper has been made it is either cut into sheets and packed, or—if required for the current stamps of Great Britain—cut into lengths of exact size and reeled. In the latter case the reels, each of which weighs 400 lb., are carefully packed in sealed containers ready for despatch to the printing works.

The next step is to gum the paper. On arrival at the printing works the rolls are taken by overhead crane to the gumming room, which is kept at a high temperature because considerable heat is required for drying the gum quickly. The gum-arabic used is the purest obtainable and comes from the Sudan where it exudes naturally as sap from the bark of various species of acacia trees.

FRACTURING THE GUM

After picking up the gum on the gumming machine the paper passes through a drying chamber and over a cold roller to ensure pliability. The reel is then treated in the fracturing machine, where the paper slides over a keen knife. The object is to crack the surface of the gum on each stamp into minute fragments. The process does no harm to the paper itself, and the effect is to prevent stretching and curling at subsequent operations. A stamp that has been damped and dried, thus undoing the good work of the fracturing machine, curls itself into a cylinder.

The gummed roll now passes to a calendering machine, the polished steel rollers of which impart a smooth finish to the surface of the paper. The paper is then re-reeled and split into two rolls, and the edges are trimmed.

The design of the stamp to be printed will have been decided long before printing begins. Stamp-designing has developed on widely different lines in different countries; stamps of Great Britain have in the main depicted only the head of the Sovereign. The designers of the earliest stamps apparently sought for an ideal type for their picture rather than a realistic portrait. A good example of this is seen in the profile of Queen Victoria on the 1840 "penny black".

This profile of the queen of 1837 was used successively for all the stamps of Great Britain throughout Victoria's

long reign. When, in 1902, the profile of Queen Victoria was replaced by that of King Edward VII, a profile sketch made by an Austrian sculptor named Emil Fuchs was used as a model. On the other hand, for the first George V stamps, issued on Coronation Day, 22nd June 1911, the head used was taken from a photograph selected by the King.

This was superseded twelve months later by a new design in which the coinage head, prepared by Sir Bertram Mackennal, was incorporated. This head, which was in true profile, was used in all later Georgian issues, including those commemorating the British Empire Exhibition and Silver Jubilee. The head of the King in current stamps is also from a photograph.

The preparation of the suggested designs is followed by printing trials, essays in colour, and variations in many points of detail, all of which call for meticulous attention before the design can be finally passed as being suitable for reproduction.

There are several methods used for printing. Until 1934, the stamps of Great Britain were produced by surface printing. The process, first used in 1855 for fiscal stamps, gradually came to be applied to postage stamps of all values.

SURFACE PRINTING

In surface printing, the design for the stamp is engraved in relief on a steel die, and after hardening this is impressed several times on to a sheet of lead, thus forming a number of matrices in which the design is in recess. The actual printing plate is formed by clamping the matrices together in a printer's "chase". This is then suspended in an electrotyping bath in which copper is electrically deposited so as to build up a thin shell that repeats the design of the stamp over its surface. When the shell has attained a sufficient thickness

STAMP PRINTING BY SURFACE PROCESS

Close-up of part of a surface press, on which stamps are printed from a cylindrical electroplate containing a series of repeated impressions of the design originally engraved on a steel die. The surface is hardened, and the electroplate is mounted on steel.

it is removed from the matrices and strengthened by a backing of type metal. It is mounted on steel, the surface is hardened and is ready for printing.

Proofs are taken on ordinary coloured paper, no white paper being allowed in the works with the exception of the water-marked paper for the stamps. Any minute differences in height in the plate are rectified in the usual way in printing—by inserting layers of paper between the plate and the bed of the press, or around the cylinder that impresses the sheets of paper on to the plate in printing. When all adjustments have been made, the actual coloured ink to be used is proofed on water-marked paper, and if approved printing proceeds in the ordinary way (Fig. 1).

When they come from the presses, the sheets are counted out and passed to the perforating machines. Here pins are arranged in a comb-like formation so as to perforate the stamps on three sides at each punch (Fig. 2). Perforating of stamps was made practical in 1850 by Edwin Hill, the brother of Rowland Hill, in conjunction with Warren de la Rue. The principle had been invented some years previously by Henry Archer, an Irishman, the method being generally and officially adopted in 1854. After being perforated, the sheets are carefully examined for defects—a close check being maintained on all spoilt sheets—and passed for trimming.

Very few imperfect stamps escape the keen eyes of the checkers. Should a sheet show a defect, it is cancelled by black lines printed across the face of the stamps. The slightest sign of misprinting or variation of colour, any white mark indicating a fold in the paper or a pin-point of oil, leads to

HOW STAMPS ARE PRINTED: ALL STAGES FROM THE ARRIVAL OF

The rolls of paper (1 & 2) are first gummed and dried (3 & 4), then the gum is fractured (5) to prevent curling. The calendering machine (6) imparts a smooth finish, after which the rolls are split (7) ready for printing. The photogravure method (8) dates from 1934. The printed

THE WATER-MARKED PAPER TO THE DISPATCH OF THE STAMPS

rolls then go through the drying room (9) to the perforating and counting machines (10 & 11). Checking and marking (12) are most important. After this the sheets are cut and trimmed (13) and are then ready for the final check (14) before being dispatched to stores.

rejection of the whole sheet. Defective impressions and stamps containing errors are most highly prized by the philatelist, but inspection of stamp dealers' catalogues shows that only very rarely does the British Post Office provide such varieties.

The perfect sheets of stamps are counted, checked yet once again, and made up into parcels, the wastage being parcelled separately. The sheets of stamps are counted, or "told", and tied in "lifts" of 25 and again in hundreds. They are next "over-told", and are finally made up into sealed parcels of 1,000 sheets, the parcel being signed by the two tellers concerned and by the supervisor, and sent to the Stamp Section of the Stores Department for issue as required by Post Offices throughout the country. The close control exercised on production is carried to the storing and issuing departments,

where all supplies are kept under lock and key in safes and strong-rooms. No issues are made from these stocks except in the presence of two officers, one of whom is always detailed each day from a rota of officers.

When a new ten-year printing contract was placed, on 1st January 1934, it was given to a new firm, and it was stipulated that the stamps concerned were to be produced by the process known as photogravure, which had already been used for the stamps of a few other countries—notably Egypt.

The new process involved special machinery for gumming, printing, and perforating the stamps direct from the reel of paper, instead of printing and perforating in sheets as had been the case previously. But it was necessary to counteract the distortion of the paper caused by the heavy printing pressure required to produce stamps to the

FORTY-SEVEN PERFORATIONS PER MOVEMENT

Fig. 2. *This is the machine which, by a comb-like arrangement of pins, perforates the stamp sheets so that the stamps are readily separable. A single punch perforates each stamp on three sides. The perforation of stamps did not become practicable until 1850.*

STAMPS FOR SLOT MACHINES

Fig. 3. *Outside most large post offices is a slot machine from which stamps may be obtained after closing time. Special single-width rolls of stamps are cut for use in these machines.*

necessary standard of perfection.

When these difficulties had been overcome the Department (late in 1934) was faced with the problem of the special Jubilee stamp. This was of a different size and unusual design, and required no fewer than seven printing tones to ensure faithful reproduction. Despite the fact that there was little margin of time, however, the necessary supplies were available by the prescribed date.

Much of the process of the actual making of stamps is secret, as with the printing of banknotes. It is very difficult for any one but an authorised official to visit the printing works of the firms who print stamps, for they are among the most carefully guarded premises in the country. And, indeed, unless one is familiar with the technicalities of printing processes, the interior is not of great interest. The uninitiated will see only

stamps everywhere—thousands, tens of thousands, hundreds of thousands of them. There are red stamps, green stamps, blue stamps; piled sheets of stamps on tables, festoons of stamps hanging from the roof, huge rolls of stamps on the floor, bundles of stamps on trolleys—and every second, throbbing printing machines are issuing more and more stamps.

The actual printing, as we have seen, is now done by photogravure, a process that gives very pleasing results. The printing is done from a copper cylinder on which the oft-repeated stamp design is etched with myriads of minute squares or dot-hollows. This cylinder is brought into contact with the ink roller, thus picking up a thin coating of ink. A "wiping knife" then takes off the ink *from the surface* of the engraved cylinder, but leaves ink in the dot-hollows. Paper brought into contact with the cylinder

MAKING BOOKS OF STAMPS

Fig. 4. *The familiar books of stamps are made up by machine-sewing sheets of stamps cut from rolls into place with the covers and intervening advertisement pages.*

picks up the ink from these hollows in quantities that vary with the depth of the cells. The variation in depth controls the tone—the light and shade—of the finished production. Where the darkest tones are required the cells are deepest, carrying a greater charge of ink for transfer to the paper; where the lightest tones are required, they are etched only to a microscopic extent. Between these two extremes there is an infinite range of depth of cells, and consequently of tones obtainable. Since copper is a soft metal, the wear and tear on the printing cylinder is reduced by chromium plating.

After passing under the printing cylinder, the paper—now a continuous sheet of stamps—is hung for a short time in long festoons for final drying.

The sheets receive serial numbers at regular intervals to form a check at a later stage. These "controls", consisting of letters and figures, and also a series of smaller figures indicating the respective printing cylinders, appear on the margins of the sheets. They are sought after by collectors, who are sometimes willing to pay high prices for them.

When the ink is dry the sheets pass to the perforating machines, some of which perforate sheets, others continuous rolls (Fig. 3). The latter are required for the automatic machines now so numerous, in which more than 800,000 rolls are used each year. Intricate apparatus (Fig. 4) turns printed sheets into books of stamps, and over 30,000,000 of these are taken into use in the course of each year.

TOBACCO AND CIGARETTES

*How Tobacco is Grown. Harvesting and Curing. Drying and Conditioning.
Cutting and Cleaning. Making Cigarettes.- Packing. How Cigars are made.
Pipe Tobacco and its Blending. Box-making Machinery.*

TOBACCO gets its name from an instrument, very much like a small hollow catapult, by which the Indians of North America inhaled through the nostrils the smoke from the burning leaves of the plant. It is a far cry from this primitive means of enjoying tobacco to the carefully blended, finely made cigarette or cigar of today.

There are some fifty varieties of the tobacco plant, but only three are cultivated extensively in order to provide the enormous quantities of tobacco which smokers need each year. To give them their botanical names, they are:— *Nicotiana tabacum, Nicotiana rustica* and *Nicotiana Persica*. The first is the most important, for it is the famous Virginia tobacco so widely in use. Latakia, distinctive in colour and flavour and used only for pipe-smoking mixtures, receives its name from Latakia, in Syria, where it is largely grown; it also is a member of the

OPENING CASKS OF TOBACCO IN THE FACTORY

Fig. 1. *From the bonded warehouse leaf tobacco goes to the factory leaf room in casks or tierces, where it is graded and blended; it then passes to the conditioning room.*

Nicotiana tabacum species. The second, *Nicotiana rustica*, first found in Mexico, was also used by the North American Indians, and the third, *Nicotiana Persica*, found largely, as its name denotes, in Iran (Persia), produces the famous Shiraz tobacco, usually considered too mild and delicate in flavour to be suitable for Western palates.

CLIMATE AND FLAVOUR

Tobacco is grown in almost every part of the world, as far north as Sweden and as far south as Chile. Although the plant adapts itself to extremes of climate, weather conditions have a tremendous effect upon its flavour and quality; it is the special soil and climate of Cuba and North America, for example, which make those countries particularly suitable for producing the tobaccos of distinctive flavours for which they are famous.

The seed beds are selected on sheltered pieces of ground with a southern aspect. The soil, which must be loamy and mellow, is first burnt to a depth of three inches in order to deposit the necessary potash to kill all weeds. A single tobacco plant can produce as many as a million seeds, and a tablespoonful of these will cover a bed a hundred square yards in area. To protect the young plants from insects and climatic variations, the beds are covered with cheesecloth. When the plants are four or six inches high and bear four to six leaves, they are ready for transplanting. Great care has to be taken to keep the roots of the plants moist and cool at this stage, and only the hardiest are selected for transplanting to fields which have been heavily ploughed and repeatedly broken up, in preparation to receive the young plants. The delicate, hair-like roots of the tobacco plant cannot survive the conditions they meet in lumpy ground.

There are about 4,200 plants to the acre and these are set by hand at intervals of three or four feet in rows from one and a half to three and a half feet apart. As excessive moisture kills the young plants, they are usually set in ridges so that the surface water can easily drain away.

When the tobacco plants have reached a certain stage of development they are topped. Topping is the process of removing the flower buds and top leaves; this causes the remaining leaves to spread out and increase in size. The growth of the plant is carefully controlled, and from ten to sixteen leaves only are left on the stem according to the development required. As they ripen the leaves change from a dark green to a lighter shade of the same colour mottled with patches of yellow.

HARVESTING THE CROP

To yield its maximum quality and flavour the tobacco crop must be harvested at the proper stage of maturity, which is usually the hottest period of the year. With "primed" tobacco, that is with leaf of high quality, two or three leaves at a time are picked from the bottom of the plant as they ripen. They are then attached with string to sticks and left to wilt in the sun before being removed to the drying sheds for curing. In the other method of harvesting the whole plant is cut down, and when sufficiently wilted is speared at the bottom of the stalk and threaded on to a lath. A space of about six inches is allowed between each two plants so treated. The laths are then carted to the curing barns. This method produces a tobacco having more "body" than the primed leaf, as much of the contents of the main stalk go into the leaf during the curing process.

There are a number of methods of curing tobacco, including flue, sun and

YOUNG SEEDLINGS COVERED WITH CHEESE CLOTH

THREAD-LIKE ROOTS

YOUNG PLANTS

HARVESTING PRIMING METHOD

TOBACCO PLANT

HARVESTING WHOLE PLANTS

BASKETS OF CURED LEAF

FIRING METHOD OF CURING

TIERCES PACKED FOR EXPORT

GROWING, CURING AND PACKING TOBACCO

Grown in beds under a protective covering, the young seedlings are later transplanted in fine soil which will not damage their roots. Harvesting can be done either by the priming method, which is to cut separate leaves, or by taking the whole plant. The tobacco is then cured by sun and air or fire, and is ready for auction and export.

E.T.T.S.—D

air curing, and firing. These methods are usually applied to whole-plant tobacco, the leaf being cured while still attached to the main stalk. Many popular brands of Virginia cigarettes are made entirely from flue-cured tobacco. In this method the system of heating consists of sheet-iron flues connected with a furnace running across the floor of the barn. The sticks or laths of leaves hang from their poles. Great care is taken that no smoke comes in contact with the leaf.

STAGES OF CURING

The three stages of curing are:—

(A) *Yellowing the leaf.* In this process the temperature is raised from 80° to 120° F. over a period of twenty-four to thirty-six hours.

(B) *Fixing the colour.* Allowing plenty of ventilation, the heat is increased to 140° F. over a period of ten to eighteen hours in order to fix the shade of colour required.

(C) *Drying the stem.* The ventilation is removed and the heat raised to 170° F. by increases of 5° an hour until the stems are dried out completely.

In fire-curing, slow wood fires are lighted in trenches running across the barn floor, the smoke coming into direct contact with the tobacco leaf. The temperature is raised to 150° F. and maintained at this heat for a period of a week to ten days, or in some cases even for as long as six weeks. Unless an even temperature is maintained the leaves, which still contain a good deal of moisture, again become soft.

Air-curing is a natural process, the leaves being hung in the barns and exposed to the air for about two months. Except that for a short period when it is first picked the tobacco leaf is left exposed to the rays of the sun, sun-curing is very similar to air-curing.

Cured leaves, being dry and brittle, are exposed to the air as they hang in the barns until they have absorbed sufficient moisture to become soft and pliable. They are then sorted into grades, lengths and qualities consistent with their colour, and tied into bundles of about fifteen leaves to be despatched to the auction warehouse, where sales are conducted with remarkable speed.

On leaving the auction warehouse the tobacco is passed through a drying machine which expels any remaining excess moisture. The leaves are then carefully packed in layers in large wooden hogsheads or tierces, and compressed into a solid mass by hydraulic rams. This compression ensures that they mellow evenly. The leaves are then removed for storage in great bonded warehouses, where they remain for several years to "age" and mature before being manufactured into the tobacco we know. As many as seventy thousand 900 lb. hogsheads of tobacco can be stored in one of these vast warehouses in Great Britain. No duty is paid to the Customs and Excise authorities until the tobacco is withdrawn from the bonded warehouse for manufacturing.

BLENDING AND CONDITIONING

Tobacco in its various manufactured forms—cigarettes, cigars, mixtures, cut cake, plug, shags and twists—involves many complicated processes. When it is released from the bonded warehouses it is first taken to the leaf room of the factory and removed from the tierces in which it was stored (Fig. 1). It is again carefully graded and blended, the blending process being most important, as it ensures the consistent flavour and quality of the finished product.

Before it is suitable for manufacture, the dry leaf must be damped in steaming and conditioning rooms (Fig. 2). The tobacco is fed on to copper mesh belts and so conveyed through a series of rotating chambers filled with steam.

TOBACCO IN THE CONDITIONING ROOM

Fig. 2. *Conditioning is the very important process by which tobacco is "cased" or matured; it mellows, sweetens and brings out the flavour. Above is a corner of the conditioning room with the stripped or stemmed leaf built up into beds or heaps.*

When it is sufficiently workable, the midrib or stem of the leaf is usually removed, as it is considered too tough and coarse for certain types of manufacture. However, in "bird's-eye" mixture it is the section of cut stalk which gives this particular tobacco its characteristic appearance.

In Great Britain manufactured tobacco must not, by law, contain over 32 per cent of moisture. It must not contain any substance other than oils essential for flavouring, and only 4 per cent of olive oil is allowed for use in spinning and making up roll tobacco.

The leaves are stemmed either by machinery or by hand. In the latter method, women working at extraordinary speed remove the stem and

deposit the leaf in heaps in one rapid movement. The heaps are built into beds and left to "case", a maturing process which mellows and sweetens the tobacco and brings out its natural flavour. It is at this stage that sweetening materials such as sugar, glycerine or liquorice are added to certain classes of tobacco; but in Great Britain the addition of flavouring material or ingredients of this nature, apart from the essential oils already mentioned, is permitted only in case of bonded factories.

In the manufacture of cigarettes or pipe mixtures, the tobacco is taken from the conditioning rooms to the cutting rooms. Forty or fifty cutting machines may be housed in one room in the larger factories. These intricate

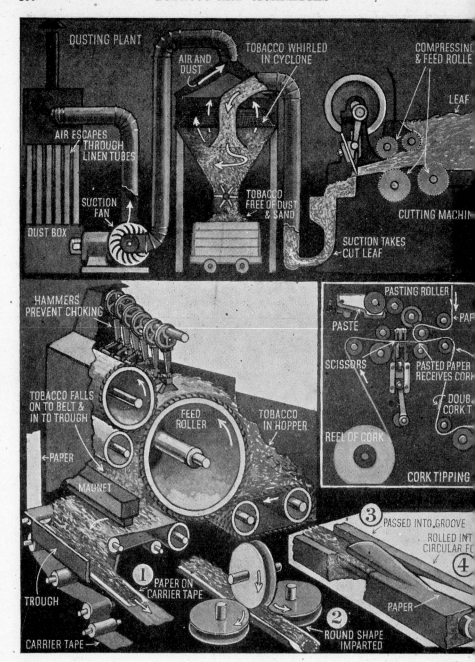

DUSTING PLANT

TOBACCO WHIRLED IN CYCLONE

AIR AND DUST

COMPRESSING & FEED ROLLE

LEAF

AIR ESCAPES THROUGH LINEN TUBES

SUCTION FAN

DUST BOX

TOBACCO FREE OF DUST & SAND

CUTTING MACHIN

SUCTION TAKES CUT LEAF

HAMMERS PREVENT CHOKING

PASTING ROLLER

PASTE

PAF

SCISSORS

PASTED PAPER RECEIVES CORK

TOBACCO FALLS ON TO BELT & IN TO TROUGH

FEED ROLLER

TOBACCO IN HOPPER

DOUB. CORK T

←PAPER

MAGNET

REEL OF CORK

CORK TIPPING

3 PASSED INTO GROOVE

ROLLED INT CIRCULAR F

4

I PAPER ON CARRIER TAPE

TROUGH

PAPER

CARRIER TAPE→

2 ROUND SHAPE IMPARTED

HOW THE CURED TOBACCO IS TURNED INTO

Tobacco enters the factory (top right) and reaches the cutting machine. It passes through revolving cylinders emerging light and fluffy; all dust is removed and it travels down a

STEMMING THE LEAF

OPENING TIERCE OF CURED LEAF

RECONDITIONING PLANT

STACK OF INSIDE WRAPPERS

ENTERING INSIDE WRAPPER

TYPE ROLLER

PAPER TO CORK TIPPING GEAR

INK

PER

FOLDING FLAPS

STACK OF OUTERS

CIGARETTES STACKED IN HOPPER

ELECTRICAL DETECTOR CHECKS 20

ABC CIGARETTES

ABC CIGARETTES

ABC CIGARETTES

ABC CIGARETTES

NTING THE BRAND MARK

PACK PUSHED INTO OPENED OUTER

PACKED 20

VIBRATING COLUMNS

ELECTRIC DRYER

PASTE POT

⑥

⑤

PASTED OVERLAP

DELIVERY CHUTES

⑦

⑧

FEED BELT

ROTATING KNIFE

ALTERNATE CIGARETTES FLICKED TO ONE SIDE

ING DISC

CIGARETTES AT THE RATE OF 30,000 AN HOUR

chute containing cigarette paper (1 and 2) in which it is rolled and gummed (3, 4, 5 and 6), cut into cigarette lengths (7 and 8), delivered in tens or twenties and packed in cartons.

machines receive the tobacco by means of a feed at the rear. It is lightly compressed and then mechanically propelled forward at a constant speed until it reaches the machine knives.

After cutting, the tobacco, which is now recognisable as that used in many of the popular brands of cigarettes, is passed through heated revolving cylinders which loosen the shreds and make them light and fluffy. This important operation of slightly drying the tobacco ensures that it loses none of its essential properties and seals its characteristic flavour. Carried along on conveyor belts, the tobacco is next put through revolving drums containing a series of sieves, through which is drawn a current of cold air. In this way particles of stem or dust are extracted. Finally, to make sure that there are no remaining impurities, the tobacco is discharged on to a further slow-moving conveyor belt and examined by hand before being packed into tins and removed to storage rooms, where it is again left to cool and mature (Fig. 3). The final cooling process takes about two days, at the end of which time the tobacco is in perfect condition and ready for manufacture.

CIGARETTE MAKING MACHINES

By far the greatest bulk of tobacco is consumed in the form of cigarettes, and machines which are true marvels of engineering skill produce these by the million. They are set up in vast machine rooms and operated by highly-skilled men and women workers. The machines are loaded with the shredded tobacco, with reels of paper more than two miles in length, tipping material in the case of cork-tipped cigarettes, printing ink for the imprint of the particular brand in manufacture and paste for sealing the edges of the cigarettes.

When the tobacco is removed from the storage rooms and taken to the machine rooms, it is tipped out of the storage tins, separated and then automatically fed into the back of the cigarette-making machine by means of large hoppers. Two carded drums control the amount passing through the machine into the trough of cigarette paper, and these drums are carefully set to ensure even filling and packing of each cigarette made. On the latest type of machine there is a special device which again extracts any remaining particles of dust and stem.

PRINTING THE BRAND NAME

Spiked rollers revolving at a high speed send the shredded tobacco down a wide chute into the narrow trough containing the cigarette paper, which is mechanically drawn along in an endless stream from a large reel of paper fitted to the back of the machine. The special printing press attached to each machine prints the registered name of the brand in exactly the right position on each length of cigarette paper before it reaches the narrow filling trough.

By a remarkable mechanical process, the loose tobacco which has fallen from the chute on to the swiftly-moving cigarette paper is next drawn into a long tube to emerge in the shape of a never-ending cigarette. In a further process the machine pastes one edge of the cigarette paper, folds it over the tobacco and then seals the lap by means of an electrical heater. Finally, rapidly revolving knives cut the long roll of tobacco into cigarette lengths. The whole series of processes of this intricate machine is carried out in almost less time than it should take the average person to read this description.

The completed cigarettes fall on a moving band from which they are weighed and examined and then packed on to trays by hand. They are then removed to special rooms and left to

EXAMINATION OF PARTLY DRIED TOBACCO

Fig. 3. *To ensure that no impurities remain in it, the tobacco is examined on a slow-moving conveyor belt before being packed in tins and put into storage rooms where it is left to cool for about two days, when it is at last ready for manufacture.*

condition for a specified time before being taken to the packing rooms.

The same ingenuity and skill is employed in the packing of cigarettes by machines which have been evolved to make them up into the familiar packets and boxes, and which almost do away with any handling.

The cigarettes are fed into hoppers or funnels fixed to the machines. The machine separates them into two layers of five or two layers of ten, according to the size of the packets to be filled, and deposits the neat bundles on to a conveyor belt which passes beneath an electrical device to detect any shortage. In normal times the cigarettes then moved along the belt to a foil-wrapping machine, which automatically wrapped the cigarettes in tin foil, a process so

rapidly carried out that the speed of the travelling conveyor was in no way slackened. The bundles move on to the next stage of the packing process, in which they are pushed by a clever device into the shaped inner case of the packet, this, by a simple mechanical operation, being timed to appear just at the right moment.

The wrapped cigarettes, now packed in their inner case, are switched to another conveyor and move along to receive their outer casing. These cartons are packed flat into the machine, but they are mechanically opened out and guided into their correct position to receive the inner carton. Here a detector device automatically ejects faulty packets. The perfect packets may then be carried by conveyor to a farther part of the machine which pushes set numbers of them into outer cartons. The heavy dispatch wrapper is added by hand, and the cigarettes are then ready to be sent off for sale to the consumer.

CIGAR MAKING

The manufacture of cigars is divided into two main categories—mould-made and hand-made cigars. In hand-made cigars the leaves are called "fillers", and these are built in the hand until they resemble the shape of the cigar. The fillers are then wrapped in a leaf known as a "bunchwrapper", the whole constituting what is called a "cigar bunch". When a final wrapper is wound around the bunch in spiral fashion, the cigar is finished. By visualising the perfect shape of the hand-made cigar, some idea can be gained of the delicacy and skill needed by the workers who wrap the tobacco.

In the manufacture of mould-made cigars the fillers are placed in a mould by hand, or wrapped in leaf by machines and then pressed into the cigar shape by means of hand-worked presses. Thereafter operators roll the bunches spirally into their final wrappers.

SORTING AND DRYING

At this stage the cigars are put through a process which can be carried out only by experts possessing the keenest sight and a high sense of shading and colouring. These experts first sort the cigars into three colours and then into half a dozen shades of each colour. The cigars of similar shade are packed into drying boxes containing quantities of twenty-five, fifty or a hundred and subjected to further pressure in their boxes. They are then banded, placed in storage boxes and removed to special rooms where they are left for a considerable period to mature before they are prepared for despatch and sale.

The processing of pipe tobacco is much the same as preparing cigarette tobaccos, but there are several popular types such as flakes, shags, plugs, twists and navy cut which are known as spun tobaccos and require certain individual processes. High grade navy cut, for instance, is still quite largely prepared in the fashion employed by the blue-jackets from whom it derives its name. Formerly, sailors were permitted to buy the unprepared leaf. This they rolled themselves, coiling string tightly around the outside.

Today, with the fine quality navy cut, the bars or plugs are moulded in the first stages by machine pressure, but are finally tightly corded, much as was the custom with the sailors, and left to condition for a number of weeks.

PRESSING PIPE TOBACCO

With ordinary navy cut, the prepared leaf is made into the desired size and shape of plug or bar by being placed in iron moulds and compressed by hydraulic presses (Fig. 4). Single leaves of particular size and quality are selected by hand and then wrapped around the plugs or bars, which are again subjected to hydraulic pressure for a period of several days. At length, the now very solid bars are machine cut and packed in the unseparated form in which the pipe smoker receives them—it is left to the smoker to rub them before filling his pipe.

Flake tobacco is processed largely in the same way, except that the prepared leaf is compressed into large flat cakes; in the case of dark flake tobacco the cakes are heated under pressure before they are ready to undergo the final period of pressing.

Spun tobacco is the only tobacco in which it is permitted to add the four per cent of pure olive oil mentioned earlier. The oil is added when the

HYDRAULIC PRESSES FOR PLUG AND FLAKE TOBACCO

Fig. 4. *Cake or flake tobacco is subjected to hydraulic pressure for a period of several days, the prepared and carefully selected leaf being first placed in iron moulds.*

E.T.T.S.—D*

tobacco is passing through the spinning machine in the process of being made into coils, thus preventing the coils from sticking together.

Twist also is manufactured in this way. The prepared leaves are spun into ropes, varying in thickness from one-eighth to one-and-a-quarter inches, by machines not unlike those used for making hemp ropes. The spun ropes of tobacco are automatically formed into coils which are corded and then baked in presses heated by steam. The same hydraulic pressure as is employed in the manufacture of navy cut is applied, and the heat and pressure turn the tobacco from its natural colour into a black roll. When it is required to retain the natural colour, as in brown roll, no oil is added and no heat applied.

The fluffiness and lightness which characterise shag tobaccos is obtained by the very fine cutting of the prepared leaf, which is afterwards baked and passed over heated copper trays made up of mechanism which separates the slices. A hard stover constantly manipulates the tobacco so that it will be uniform and consistent, and it is then left to cool.

Latakia, Cavendish, Eastern and Turkish tobaccos have very distinctive flavours, but when blended with more delicate tobacco, such as Virginia, make a popular mixture. The processing of these mixtures is similar to that already described except that an additional process is necessary for the purpose of mixing the various blends. This is done mechanically. In some cases special shapes are moulded in order to produce the distinctive cuts which

MAKING CARDBOARD BOXES AND CARTONS

Fig. 5. *Box-making machines are among the most ingenious to be seen in a tobacco factory. Sheets of plain, flat cardboard having been fed into these machines emerge as complete boxes with edges trimmed, to prevent dust collecting, and printed and coloured.*

MACHINE PACKING IN AIR-TIGHT TINS

Fig. 6. *Packed in this way tobacco will retain its fresh and moist condition for a very long time. The tobacco is weighed and packed by hand into the tins which pass through a vacuumising machine which extracts the air and seals the tin.*

provide a slow-burning and cool smoke.

The various kinds of pipe tobaccos are removed to the packing and despatch departments. Again, machinery carries out this last process of packing the tobacco in tin foil or in air-tight tins. Women weigh it into required quantities and each heap is tipped into a small chamber forming part of a round rotating counter. Hoppers receive the tobacco and convey it to mechanical presses which compress it into the required shape, and wrap it in foil and paper automatically fed into the machine. It travels on another conveyor to the labelling and wrapping part of the machine, and emerges in an outer wrapper of moisture-proof, transparent tissue, which also helps to keep the tobacco in prime condition. Tobacco packed by a vacuum process retains its full flavour and fresh condition for an

indefinite period; it is made air-tight by placing the filled tins in the vacuum machine which extracts the air and automatically seals the tins (Fig. 6).

Many large, modern factories have their own box-making departments, and the machinery used in their manufacture is no less ingenious than that employed in making tobaccos. The plain cardboard is fed into a machine (Fig. 5) composed of six units. It finally emerges in the familiar shape and form after being punched into outer and inner cartons, rimmed, the lids domed, the edges trimmed to prevent dust collecting, and printed and coloured.

The tobacco in all its forms and varieties is now ready for the smoker. Endless moving belts convey it to the loading decks of the despatch departments, and so it begins its long journey to smokers in all parts of the world.

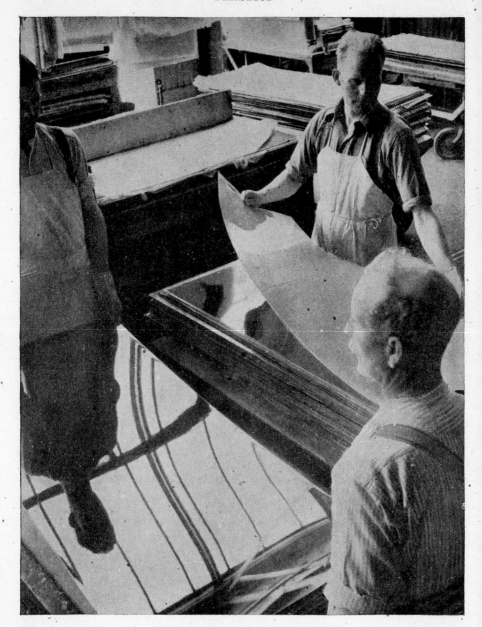

POLISHING XYLONITE SHEETS

Fig. 1. *Many of the uses to which xylonite is put require that it should be highly polished, chiefly in the case of the thinner sheets. This is done by heating and cooling it under high pressure in contact with nickel plates, whose mirror surface is taken by the sheets when sufficiently heated to become temporarily plastic. Sheets of the polished xylonite are seen being removed from the plates on which they have been heated.*

PLASTICS

Nitro-Cellulose and Xylonite. Centrifuging and Colouring. Polishing. Rods and Tubes. Thermo-Plastics and Resinoids. Fillers. Bakelite. Moulding Processes. Making Telephone Mouthpieces.

SINCE the beginning of the present century an ever-increasing assortment of everyday objects has been derived from substances that would have greatly startled our grandparents; such as gun-cotton, disinfectants and milk. From one or more of these improbable raw materials most of our buttons, fountain pens, pipe-stems and cigarette holders are made; so, too, are the handles of our umbrellas, our toothbrushes, shaving brushes, hair brushes and other toilet gear; the pumps, chainguards and handle grips of our bicycles; ornaments on dresses, hats and shoes; and even imitation precious stones.

All these things are made of plastics. Wood has to be fashioned by cutting and finished by painting or polishing. Metal can be stamped or moulded, but even more than wood needs a protective covering. So, too, does china, which has the added disadvantage of extreme fragility. How much easier, and consequently cheaper, to make these intricately-shaped objects and gadgets by squirting into moulds a soft substance that will set hard and strong, and be impervious to moisture and heat, without the necessity for costly finishing!

GUN-COTTON AND CELLULOSE

The plastics industry, which has achieved these substances and this method, is a new industry in the sense that it has been rapidly developed in the last few years. Its origins date back to the middle of last century, when chemists were much interested in the newly discovered explosive gun-cotton.

Gun-cotton is cellulose treated with nitric and sulphuric acids, and this nitro-cellulose was converted into a solid ivory-like material by Alexander Parkes of Birmingham. From Parkes' experiments there emerged the stuff now known to everyone as celluloid.

Celluloid soon proved to possess extremely useful properties. It could be made transparent or opaque, plain or coloured; it was tough and strong and proof against air, water and acids; it could be softened by moderate heat, and in that state rolled into sheets of any thickness or moulded into any desired shape. Its great drawback was its extreme inflammability. Gun-cotton, when uncompressed, burns in a very leisurely way, but its cousin celluloid used to go off with a flash until means were discovered for restraining it.

USES OF XYLONITE

Purged of its early defects, nitro-cellulose, which was the first in the field of commercial plastics, still holds its own under the trade name of xylonite, a convenient and beautiful material of countless uses. It is unrivalled where lightness, strength and transmission of light are important, and it has special advantages where fine surface patterns are wanted in the finished article.

To make xylonite, "linters", the downy coverings of the seeds of the cotton plant, are mixed with nitric and sulphuric acids of carefully controlled strength, and stirred and churned until they turn into raw nitro-cellulose. This mixture is too wet, however, so the

WASHING NITRO-CELLULOSE PULP

Fig. 2. *Raw nitro-cellulose is made by churning raw cotton with nitric and sulphuric acids. The surplus acids are removed by rapid rotation of the mass in centrifugal hydro-extractors, and then washed and bleached. Here the bleaching acids are being washed away.*

excess acid is removed by centrifugal machines called hydro-extractors. Inside a metal cylinder, fitted with a lid that can be hermetically closed, is a smaller cylinder made of perforated metal and revolving on a central axis. The wet masses of nitro-cellulose are placed in the inner cylinder, which is then rapidly rotated for a few minutes to force out the surplus moisture.

Having been "centrifuged", the pulp is boiled in order to stabilise it against changes of temperature and humidity. The next step is to bleach it, and afterwards to wash away all traces of the bleaching agents (Fig. 2). The pulp returns to the centrifugals, now for removal of the excess of washing water; and still again, this time to replace the

remaining water by alcohol (Fig. 3) When the nitro-cellulose, at this stage a flaky mass moist with alcohol, leaves the centrifuges for the last time it is ready for the camphor that transforms it into a plastic substance.

Camphor, when mixed with the cellulose pulp in kneading machines, resembling the baker's dough mixer, interacts with the cellulose, changing it from the granular or flaky consistency to a stiff, tough dough like gelatine (Fig. 4). The alcohol dissolves the camphor, ensuring its even combination with the mass. It is not required in the finished xylonite, and will be removed at a later stage of manufacture.

If coloured xylonite is wanted, the colouring material is added to the plastic mass with the camphor. Only plain colours are produced at this stage, admixtures and configurations being developed later by blending and working up the plain colours in varying proportions in subsequent processes. If no colour is added, the final product will be transparent and pale yellow—a colour that is not popular in most trades. This natural colour is usually eliminated by the addition of blue or violet colouring matter, either at this or at a later stage.

By the addition of soluble dyes, transparent colours are obtained for use in the manufacture of a wide range of transparent articles from tooth-brush handles to fog-lamp covers for motorcars. Opaque materials are produced by the addition of pigments—for instance,

white is used for imitation ivories, large quantities of which are taken by the cutlery trade for the handles of knives, forks and other articles. Delicate colours are used for the sheets from which artificial flowers will be made. Browns are used to match various leather colours for the boot and shoe industry, while a large quantity of black xylonite is made both in sheets and tubes for cycle pumps, mudguards, cycle handle grips, covering for steering wheels of motor cars, and so on.

The next thing is to filter the xylonite, for, however carefully the work was done, odd bits of foreign matter will have found their way into the ingredients and the machines to spoil the final products. Hydraulic rams, working at a

CENTRIFUGAL HYDRO-EXTRACTOR

Fig. 3. *After bleaching, the nitro-cellulose is returned to the centrifuges to remove excess water, and then yet again to replace the water by alcohol, the same machine performing both operations. Here is one of the machines in which these processes take place.*

UNLOADING A MIXER

Fig. 4. *In these mixers nitro-cellulose is mixed with camphor, leaving the machines in the form of a plastic, gelatine-like dough.*

pressure of $2\frac{1}{4}$ tons to the square inch, force the material through close-woven filter cloth, from which it emerges in strings like spaghetti (Fig. 5).

The next operation is to remove the surplus alcohol, introduced in the dehydration process, that has now served its purpose as a solvent for the camphor. The dough is then consolidated and hardened off on hot steel rollers, during which operation the material is frequently cut across and folded so as to ensure a homogeneous product. When it is judged to be sufficiently hard it is transferred to larger and slower-running rollers, and is then calendered into sheets.

Where the product is required without configuration it is cut approximately to size and a number of these sheets are assembled on a heavy cast-iron table. Here, by alternate hot and cold pressing, the separate sheets are combined into a block several inches thick. Still anchored to the iron table, the block passes to and fro beneath an inclined knife. This is accurately adjustable in height, the depth to which the knife is lowered after each stroke of the machine controlling the thickness of the sheet cut from the block. In this way perfectly even sheets are sliced off at each movement of the bed-plate (Fig. 6).

These sheets, which may be as thin as one four-thousandth of an inch or as thick as an inch or more, still contain a considerable proportion of alcohol, which must be removed before they are ready for the market. This is done by hanging the sheets in warm dry rooms until they are approximately constant in weight and shrinkage is complete. Although thin sheets can be seasoned in a few days, thicker ones may require several weeks or even months. In seasoning, some sheets may warp slightly, but this is easily put right by warming and pressing once again.

After inspection, unpolished sheets are now ready for delivery to the customer. A large proportion of the sheets are required to be polished, however, particularly the thinner sheets. They

CELLULOSE ACETATE DOUGH

Fig. 5. *Filtering the xylonite dough under heavy pressure has the effect of turning it into a spaghetti-like substance.*

are given a high enduring gloss by heating and cooling them under considerable pressure in contact with nickel plates (Fig. 1). The mirror surface of these plates is taken by the surface of the sheets when they have become temporarily plastic from being heated.

When xylonite is required in rods or tubes, the raw material—either in the form of powder or as thick sheets—is passed to extruding machines. If in the form of powder, it is thoroughly mixed while dyes are added (Fig. 7). The powder is then fed to a heated nozzle where it becomes plastic and emerges as a rod. If in sheet form, it is forced under heat and pressure through a nozzle to the required size. In this way a continuous length of rod is formed, which is known as a "nozzle rod" to distinguish it from "cut" rods. By the use of a cone or mandrel a tube will be formed. As the tubes or rods are extruded from the machine, they are cut off into convenient lengths (Fig. 10); then they are seasoned in the same way as the sheets. By cutting off suitable sections from a shaped rod, buttons, buckles and similar objects are formed.

Although an astonishing variety of xylonite objects, from table-tennis balls to mirror frames, can be produced from rods, sheets, tubes and similar machine processes, many articles are made by hand turning (Fig. 8). Skilled craftsmen are needed even in this mechanised trade for the purpose of turning out work that cannot be done as well by any existing machine (Fig. 9).

Let us now turn to a different type of plastic material. Gun-cotton gives us xylonite, which belongs to the class known as "thermo-plastics"; these can always be resoftened by heating, no matter how long they have been in a rigid non-plastic state. But there is another sort of plastics, called "thermo-setting", which includes most of the so-

called synthetic resins, or "resinoids". Their peculiarity is that they are hardened by heat, and can be moulded during the heating. But this involves a molecular change in their substance, and no further variation in shape can be effected by further heating. This is where disinfectants, urea (a constituent of urine) and milk come in useful. We will look first at the disinfectants.

One of the best known of all disinfectants is phenol or carbolic acid, which

MAKING XYLONITE SHEETS

Fig. 6. *Perfectly even sheets are sliced off at each movement of the bed-plate by a fixed knife from the solid block of material.*

is obtained from benzene, a product of gas tar. It is sold to the public only in the form of a very weak solution, but in the pure state it is a crystalline solid. Carbolic acid is turned into a most useful plastic material by the very remarkable action of another disinfectant, formaldehyde. Formaldehyde is a gas; a 40 per cent solution of it in water, known as formalin, is used as an antiseptic.

The first phenol resinoids appeared at the beginning of the present century, when Dr. Leo Hendrik Baekeland discovered how to turn liquid carbolic acid and a solution of formaldehyde into a resin-like substance that came to be called bakelite. The liquids are introduced into a reaction vessel together with a chemical "accelerator", and subjected to heat. As a result of the reaction, a viscous mass is formed at the bottom of the vessel with a layer of water above it. This deposit is bakelite resinoid, and when the water is removed it is tapped off and allowed to cool. As its temperature falls, the resinoid assumes a solid form in which it is brittle and can be fractured easily.

At this stage the resinoid can be softened by heating, or dissolved by solvents. Application of heat causes a chemical change to take place, however, for although the resinoid will soften it will then reharden to a permanently hard and insoluble state. The material in this state has been polymerised, that is to say, an entirely new molecule has been made out of several old ones by heating them up under certain conditions.

RESINOID PLASTICS

By changes in the formulas, and variations in manufacturing technique, many types of resinoids with special characteristics have been developed. The test tubes and retorts of the laboratory have given place to batteries of large stills at the bakelite works, and the chemicals that are fed into them are stored in giant containers, each having a capacity of thousands of gallons. Large quantities of moulding powders are supplied to firms who specialise in moulding a vast number of products.

The first step in the production of moulding powder is the pulverising of the resinoid in large crushing machines. When this has been done the second major ingredient, known as the "filler", is introduced, and the two powders are then thoroughly mixed together.

Fillers are of various types. The most generally used filler is wood flour, which endows the finished product with reasonably good electrical and physical properties. Most of the thousands of domestic articles moulded from bakelite materials embody a filler of this type. When it is desired that the moulding shall have great strength and be capable of high resistance to mechanical shock, the filler takes the form of small flakes or fibres of fabric. When the moulding must eventually withstand exposure to heat, an asbestos filler is adopted.

FILLER MATERIALS

Mineral fillers are also used to give low water absorption, and special fillers can be obtained that give added resistance to acids or alkalis. The selection and blending of fillers to suit certain conditions, or where special applications are desired, is a highly skilled task.

The filler having been selected, suitable pigments, mould lubricants, plasticizers, and accelerators are also introduced. These, together with the powdered resinoid, are mixed in special machines, and the powder resulting from these ingredients is fed on to heated rollers in a continuous stream. Under the influence of heat the resinoid becomes plastic, and binds the filler and pigment into a homogeneous mass. As it leaves the rollers the material has the appearance of sheet rubber, and in this form it is taken by conveyor to be crushed and sifted again. While on its journey to the crushers the material is cooled in readiness for the final grinding operation. Once the ground material has successfully passed the sieves it is fed to machines, by which it is packed in drums ready for the moulder.

The length of time that the powder spends in the rolling process is carefully controlled, since the further heating to

MIXING DYES WITH POWDERED XYLONITE

Fig. 7. *To make rods or tubes, powdered xylonite is mixed with the required dyes by swinging arms in a revolving bowl (above), and then heated till it becomes plastic.*

which it is subjected here tends to advance the resinoid a step further towards that stage when it becomes infusible and insoluble. The completion of this final hardening is, of course, left to the moulder, but the process of polymerisation must be sufficiently advanced to enable him to produce the moulded articles rapidly. Moulding is a separate branch of the industry.

The phenol-formaldehyde material is also cast in a variety of forms and is thus supplied to the user in sheets, tubes, and rods of various sections (Fig. 11). The shapes are then machined, and for this type of work, of course, no moulds are required in the production of the finished articles. Although these cast resins are comparatively expensive, the fact that there are no mould costs makes them a useful material for small quantities of some particular article. The materials, which are translucent and can be obtained in a range of very attractive colours, are widely used for the manufacture of such articles as buttons and ornaments.

Bakelite, however, is only one of the group of synthetic resins—the phenol group—known as the thermo-setting type. Another synthetic resin—or resinoid—of the thermo-setting type is made from urea. The function of the kidneys in animals is to remove from the blood the useless waste products, of which the most difficult to eliminate are the large molecules of broken-down protein. Proteins are compounds of nitrogen; and the kidneys reduce them, by oxidation, to what is believed to be the final product of such nitrogenous compounds in animals. This is the substance called urea. Its great advantage

industrially is that it can be produced in the laboratory without assistance from kidneys or any other animal organs.

The attraction of the ureas as thermosetting plastics lies in the wide range of light colours, including a very pure white, in which they can be produced. The phenol group, on the other hand, provides dark colours, mainly black, browns and dark reds. When what is known as a paper filler is used in the process of moulding the urea resinoids, the resulting articles are translucent, giving them added lustre and beauty.

Milk also contains protein in the form of casein. This is the nitrogenous matter in milk which makes a tough curd when the milk goes sour. It has a very complicated molecule in which carbon, hydro-

CRAFTSMANSHIP IN MODERN MATERIAL

Fig. 8. *Many plastic articles are made by machine processes, but there is still scope for the skilled hand turner in this newest of industries. Here rings of xylonite are being built up into drinking vessels. Cylinders formed from the rings can be seen on the right.*

LAST STAGES OF A PLASTIC MIRROR

Fig. 9. *Many hand mirrors are nowadays framed in xylonite and other plastics. This worker is giving the final touch to these articles by polishing glass and frame on a revolving buff.*

gen, oxygen, sulphur and phosphorus become linked with the nitrogen. In cheesemaking the casein is toughened and hardened by the action of acids produced by bacteria introduced into the milk. But other things have this effect, one of them being formaldehyde.

Although chemists were well aware that formaldehyde possessed this property of toughening protein—it will make soft animal tissues as hard as leather— the discovery of its action on casein is said to have been accidental. The story goes that a research chemist one night took bread and cheese to his laboratory to sustain him while working out an experiment. He had the misfortune (as he thought) to spill some formalin over his supper, and being too much pre-occupied to throw it away he let it stay

where it was. When, hours later, the time came to clear up, he found that the cheese had become as hard as bone.

The making of moulded articles consists, briefly, of feeding pre-determined quantities of moulding material into heated moulds placed between the platens of a hydraulic press (Fig. 13). Some articles require enormous presses.

The first step is to design and make a mould. This highly skilled work is carried out by trained draughtsmen and tool-makers. Although experiments have been made with other materials, in practice the moulds are always machined from high-quality cast steel. There are usually two parts to a mould —one with a cavity in it representing the outside form of the article, and the other a solid piece of steel of which the

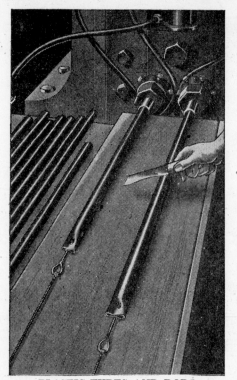

PLASTIC TUBES AND RODS

Fig. 10. *Tubes of xylonite are extruded in long sections from a shaping machine and cut off to the required length by hand. The wires steer them from the nozzles.*

outside represents the article's inside form (Fig. 14). This inner part of the mould is formed slightly less in size than the mould of the outside article, so that the space between the two parts represents the article itself. After machining, the mould must be polished to eliminate all tool marks, since even a minute mark on the mould is faithfully reproduced on the moulding. In addition, the moulds often are chromium-plated to give an extra high finish to the moulding.

Broadly speaking, moulds are classified as of the portable and the fixed—or semi-automatic—types, and then again as flash moulds and positive moulds (Fig. 15). The semi-automatic flash is the type in general use for commercial production. The "flash" is the thin film of material that appears where the two halves of the mould meet. During the moulding process the moulds must be heated; steam is generally used.

In many cases an article is required of such shape that an "undercut" is formed, that is to say, it would be impossible to extract the article from the mould were it moulded in the normal manner. For example, a cup with a handle could not be extracted from its

BUTTONS IN ENDLESS VARIETY

Fig. 11. *Buttons, buckles, and other similar objects are made by cutting sections from shaped rods formed as powdered or sheet xylonite is extruded from a machine nozzle.*

MOULDING TELEPHONE MOUTHPIECES FROM PLASTICS

Fig. 12. *One of the most familiar objects made from a plastic is the telephone mouthpiece. In the open press to the left are seen the four mouldings produced in a single operation. The operator—gloved because the mouldings issue from the press hot—can be seen in the act of fitting these parts together to form the modern telephone ear and mouthpiece.*

mould. To overcome this difficulty the bottom portion of the mould is made in two pieces. The article is pressed, the top portion of the mould raised, and the two "splits" of the bottom portion are then withdrawn horizontally. Obviously, a special type of press is required for handling such split moulds.

Another form of mould construction, known as "hobbing", is used when a large number of comparatively small articles are required. For this, a mould is made containing a number of impressions so that a number of the articles can be produced at each operation of the press. Hobbing is used where these impressions cannot readily be machined, or where they have surface designs or lettering or embossing. In this process

an exact replica of the required article is machined and hardened. This replica is then forced by pressure in a hobbing press into a softer metal, as many times as may be required, according to the number of articles to be produced from the mould. In each case the result is a complete negative mould for the required article. An average pressure in the hobbing operation would be 150 tons per square inch.

Thermo-plastic materials are usually moulded by the injection moulding process. As its name implies, the distinguishing feature of this process is the fact that the material is plasticized by heat in a special cylinder outside the mould, before being injected into the mould by a hydraulically-operated

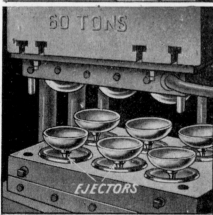

MAKING BAKELITE MOULDINGS

Fig. 13. *Powder is poured into the moulds (top), the mould closed for the baking period (centre), and the finished mouldings automatically ejected (bottom).*

plunger. This process relies on moulds of entirely different construction from those just described, the two halves of the mould being closed by pressure before the moulding, and there is no space for overflow or "flash" (Fig. 16).

The material is forced through channels that lead directly into the mould cavity through a nozzle from the separate cylinder where the powder is heated to a plastic state. The orifice in the mould is made to fit the nozzle of the injection machine, the latter being brought up to the mould before the ram forces the material into the mould. The transfer must be accomplished in the shortest possible time—about one second, under normal conditions—in order to prevent the setting of the material before the mould is completely filled. This is specially important in the case of large mouldings, or moulds carrying numerous impressions, where the plastic material is required to travel a considerable distance before filling the mould. The mould itself is cooled to allow the material to set rapidly. A very high rate of production is possible with injection-moulding presses, which are often entirely automatic. Finishing operations on injection-moulded articles are even fewer than on pressure-moulded ones, since there is only the "feed", or place where the material enters the mould, to be cleaned off.

INJECTION MOULDING

Injection moulding makes possible the production of mouldings of a shape and intricacy that cannot be achieved by other means. The process also lends itself to the moulding of thin-walled articles with flanges, such as coil formers and pen and pencil parts.

The great presses used for moulding the thermo-setting material are of many different types, but all may be divided into two main classes: the mechanical and the hydraulic. Whereas the mechanical press has a fixed stroke and speed with the end pressure indefinite, the hydraulic press is the reverse in that it has a flexible stroke and speed, with the end pressure determinable.

TYPES OF PRESS

The hydraulic press is the one most widely used, and of this type the semi-automatic is most common. Here the moulds are channelled to accommodate the heating medium, the moulded article being ejected automatically from the mould cavity. Moulding temperature varies according to the nature of the material used, and may be from 300° F. to 340° F. or even higher.

In the actual pressing operation the lower or negative part of the mould is fixed in the press, and the upper or positive portion is fixed to the movable part of the press. A carefully calculated amount of powder is placed in the lower portion and the top portion is lowered into it. Full pressure is applied when the mould is closed, when the moulding powder—becoming plastic, owing to the heat—is forced under pressure into every part of the mould. The press remains shut for the moulding to set. This is known as the "curing time", and varies according to the size and shape of the moulding and the particular grade of material adopted. It may continue for a few seconds or for several minutes. In the production of a disk 4 in. in diameter by $\frac{1}{4}$ in. thick, the time of cure will be from three to three-and-a-half minutes. Except for the removal of "fins", as a thin lip of material left around the edges of the moulding is called, the product needs no further finishing.

This easy, straightforward way of making things of intricate shapes depends on very complicated machinery. The machines are automatic, or

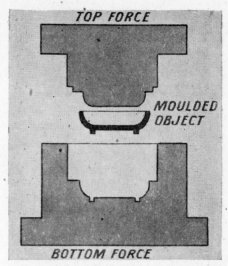

MOULD FORMS FOR PLASTICS

Figs. 14 and **15.** *Above: Positive mould. Below: General form of flash mould.*

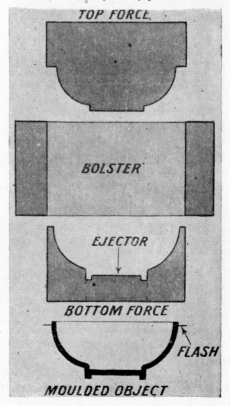

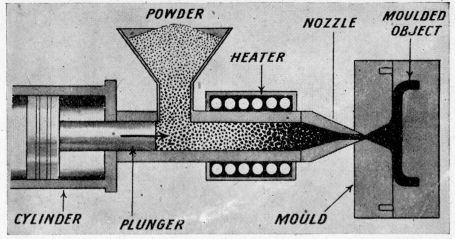

INJECTION MOULDING

Fig. 16. *In this process, usual with thermo-plastics, the material is forced into the mould through a nozzle, the two halves of the mould being closed by pressure before moulding begins.*

nearly so. The moulding powder is stored in a hopper, and a measuring contrivance doles out the exact amount required at each moulding stroke of the ram. Another contrivance controls the curing time; others, the pressure to be applied and the temperature to a degree.

Such, then, are the simplest aspects of moulding plastics, but in practice there are many very ingenious processes available where required. For instance, metal parts for a variety of purposes— such as screws and bushes—can be incorporated in moulded articles, not only eliminating a great deal of machining, but also resulting in a far better job. The metal parts to be inserted can be securely anchored in the moulding and their position accurately controlled.

An example is the plastic radio cabinet, where the loudspeaker is frequently mounted on metal inserts projecting from the inside face of the article. Similarly, in the Post Office telephone hand-piece the necessary electrical connections from the earpiece at one end to the mouth-piece at the other are moulded inside the handle.

The moulding of these articles is illustrated in Figs. 12 and 17.

Decorative patterns can easily be obtained on the surface of a moulding. Simple geometrical designs are produced on the mould in the tool shop, but the most intricate designs can be worked by specialist steel engravers. The cheaper, and therefore more usual, method is to have designs in relief on the moulding, as this necessitates merely cutting into the steel mould. On the other hand, the reverse effect, in the form of sunk designs, can be produced by cutting away the steel around the design and leaving the engraved portions standing above the surface of the mould. Another interesting development is the moulding in of decorative metal inserts in cigarette boxes and so on.

Already the plastics industry, though hardly out of its swaddling clothes, assumes the proportions of a young giant. In time, no doubt, it will supply our needs on a scale now undreamed of; in fact, we may yet travel in cars, buses, trains and ships moulded from gun-cotton, disinfectants, urea or milk.

END OF TELEPHONE MOUTHPIECE MOULDING CYCLE

Fig. 17. *The open press shows a three-impression mould. The moulder is replacing the tool inserts at the top, which form the bayonet slot recesses in the moulding. Split portions of the mould are seen in the front centre. To their left are six preformed tablets of the moulding material—in this case phenol formaldehyde; finished mouldings are seen on the extreme left. During the actual moulding process, the top part comes down and the plastic is "baked."*

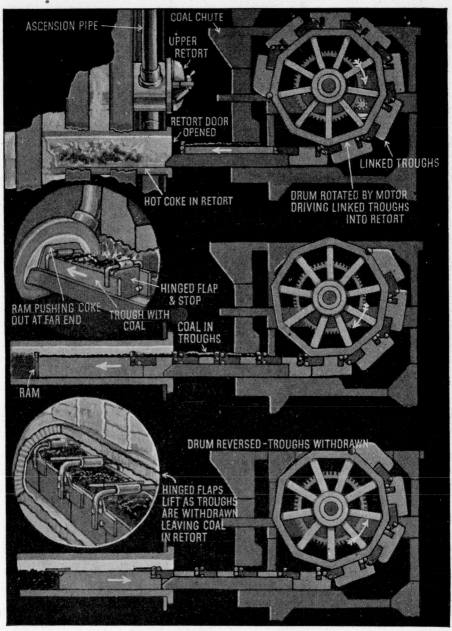

ASCENSION PIPE

COAL CHUTE

UPPER RETORT

RETORT DOOR OPENED

HOT COKE IN RETORT

LINKED TROUGHS

DRUM ROTATED BY MOTOR DRIVING LINKED TROUGHS INTO RETORT

RAM PUSHING COKE OUT AT FAR END

HINGED FLAP & STOP

TROUGH WITH COAL

COAL IN TROUGHS

RAM

DRUM REVERSED-TROUGHS WITHDRAWN

HINGED FLAPS LIFT AS TROUGHS ARE WITHDRAWN LEAVING COAL IN RETORT

CHARGING COAL INTO RETORTS

Fig. 1. *One type of machine for charging coal into a horizontal retort. The ram at the front pushes out the expended coke, the door at the far end having been previously opened by an assistant, and the gas rises through the ascension pipe. The linked troughs are so made that the coal is left in the retort automatically as they are withdrawn.*

GAS AND ITS BY-PRODUCTS

Town Lighting. History of Domestic Lighting. British Thermal Unit. Retorts, Vertical and Horizontal. Tar and Other By-Products. Carburetted Water Gas. Washing the Gas. Station Meters. Gas Holders. Domestic Meters.

To practically every city dweller the word "gas", as evoked by the familiar figure of Mr. Therm, means just the complex vapour that comes out of the burners of the cooking stove when you turn on the tap. But, properly speaking this should be qualified as fuel gas, for to the chemist a gas is any form of matter in that one of its three "states" (the others being the "solid" and "liquid" states) when the component molecules are widely separated, and we are told that nine of the elements, including the oxygen and nitrogen of which air is mainly composed, are normally in this state. But there are hundreds of other combinations of elements that exist as gases, even though some of their constituents may normally be solid. These combinations are, of course, equally entitled to the name of gas, and each of us lives only by breathing a gas—for that essentially is what air is—into his lungs and breathing another kind of gas out again.

GASES IN COMMON USE

At least a dozen different gases are in common commercial or medical use, and these are obtained without having recourse to the taps in the kitchen. The gas that comes out from the oven burners is actually a combination of about six different gases, two of which do not burn at all. When large quantities of gases are required for industrial purposes, they are in many cases bought in liquid form. Coal gas, to give it the name which most accurately describes it, is the most valuable of the many products of that wonderful black mineral that we have squandered so extravagantly during the last hundred years. Dr. John Clayton, in 1691, first drew supplies from coal, or perhaps we should say that he first discovered that the coal would emit gas when heated. Others after him carried out experiments : Hales in 1726, Lord Dundonald, who in 1787 lit the hall at Culross Abbey in Fifeshire with it, and William Murdock in 1792. Murdock's work advanced the application of coal gas still further, and his employers, Matthew Boulton and James Watt, gave permission in 1802 for him to experiment in the lighting of the great Soho engine works at Birmingham by gas.

FISH-TAIL FLAMES

Later on, when Winsor worked out a scheme for the distribution of gas by pipes buried below ground, Pall Mall in London was lit, after a fashion, by coal gas. That was in 1807. Five years later the greatest gas-making concern in the world—the Gas Light and Coke Company—received their charter. Though the gas that they made and distributed was something like the gas we know, yet if the householder of today found it coming through his pipes there would be an outcry! Not much was then known about the valuable by-products, and illumination depended entirely upon the luminous flame produced by direct burning, a most indifferent form of light. Many people can remember the fish-tail gas flame which was almost all we had at the end of the last century, and is still employed in certain types of bathroom

125

geysers and kitchen water-heaters to-day. Lighting devices incorporating these flames were seen everywhere, even in living-rooms, encircled by opal glass globes, but they were most inefficient.

Perhaps one of the greatest inventions which led up to the use of gas as an actual fuel as well as an illuminant was that of Bunsen, professor at Heidelberg University, in the 1860's. He found that the mixing of a small quantity of gas

AN UNUSUAL GASHOLDER

Fig. 2. *This spherical holder contains gas at a greater pressure than the much more familiar cylindrical type.*

with many times its volume of air produced a clean, non-luminous flame with a great intensity of heat. Moreover, it was completely sootless. This is the type of flame employed today in all gas cookers and gas fires.

Arising out of this, Welsbach produced a fabric cone that encircled the Bunsen flame, the fabric being woven from a thread called ramie, and impregnated with a rare earth named thorium that glowed brilliantly white when heated. This immediately revolutionised

gas lighting, both for street and house, and brought gas right into the foreground as a household fuel, to the position it has maintained and improved upon consistently ever since.

What is this gas, and how does it come to be available in the cold, black, stony lumps we know as coal? The latter half of the question is not so easy to answer without delving deeper into the science of chemistry than we can do here, but the former half can soon be answered. Coal gas is a mixture of six gases—in the following average proportions on a percentage basis:

Hydrogen . . .	49
Methane (Marsh Gas) .	27
Carbon monoxide . .	9
Heavy Hydrocarbons .	4
Carbon dioxide (Carbonic Acid Gas) . . .	$2\frac{1}{2}$
Nitrogen . . .	$8\frac{1}{2}$

BRITISH THERMAL UNIT

The last two are incombustible, but it is practically impossible to extract them. Gas of this quality should produce about 550 British Thermal Units from every cubic foot, assuming it to be properly applied. The British Thermal Unit is the standard British measurement unit of heat, being the amount of heat required to raise the temperature of one pound of water ($1\frac{1}{4}$ pints) from 60° to 61° Fahrenheit. This is how it works out in practice. A small pot of tea can be made with $1\frac{1}{4}$ pints of water, and if you fill the kettle with water at the normal temperature of 60° F., it will need a matter of 152 B.Th.U. to bring it up to boiling point. So a cubic foot of gas *could* make enough water hot to boil that kettle at least three times.

A therm represents 100,000 B.Th.U., and all gas suppliers are compelled, by Act of Parliament, to see to it that their gas has a certain declared and constant value in heat units. Casual

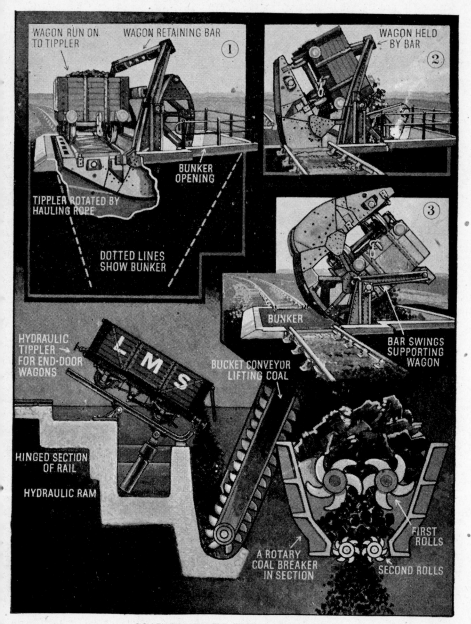

COAL COMES TO THE GASWORKS

Fig. 3. *Expeditious coal handling results from the use of wagon-tipplers, whereby a whole 10-ton wagon is emptied at a single operation. Two types are shown, that at the top for tipping from a wagon without doors, that below for use with end door wagons. Bottom right, a coalbreaker in section, showing the two sets of rotating curved knives which crush the coal to the required size in order to avoid the obstructions that large lumps would create.*

reference to a typical gas bill shows that the gas supplied has a value of 500 B.Th.U. for each cubic foot, a good easy number to reckon with, for the meter records the consumption in cubic feet only, and these must be converted to their equivalent in therms before the cost of the gas can be arrived at.

GAS ANALYSIS

But how does the gas which our meters measure come into being? And first of all, how is its parent, coal, composed? Here is a percentage analysis of a typical bituminous coal, of good quality for gas making:

Carbon	80
Hydrogen	5·5
Oxygen	8·8
Nitrogen	1·5
Sulphur	0·8
Ash	3·4

Since coal is required in large quantities, the first essential for a gas works is a site where transport is freely available. Waterborne coal comes cheapest, so river or canal sites are preferred. But there can be no hand-to-mouth methods; a big coal reserve must always be available, so space for dumping must be arranged. Travelling skips, running on suspended cables or gantry tracks, keep a continuous stream in motion from the boats' holds to the dump, and from there by way of travelling grabs to the site where the first process, that of breaking up the lumps to a small size, is carried out. A smooth flow is desired everywhere, with no risk of obstruction in narrow places by big lumps, so the coal is crushed to lumps of walnut size in rotary crushing machines (Fig. 3).

Where railway transport is the rule, the coal wagons will be run into tipplers that clamp them firmly, and then, turning them over in a heavy frame, empty the contents immediately either into bunkers or direct into the crushers.

The belt conveyor, a familiar sight at most gasworks, is a most efficient method of transporting a constant stream of coal over considerable distances. One of these conveyors may be used to keep the bunker over the retort house filled.

The coal has to be heated up to something like 2,000° F. to make it yield the maximum quantity of gas, but modern practice sacrifices some of the gas in order to get a greater proportion of that valuable by-product, tar. This so-called low-temperature carbonization yields less gas but more tar, and the tar goes to the hydrogenating plant for conversion into motor spirit, a process about which a great deal has been heard in recent years. The heating is carried out in large upright chimneys built of silica brick, a material possessing high heat-resisting quality.

An average set of dimensions of a retort, which is of rectangular section, might show a total height of 27 feet, the opening at the top being 100 in. by 10 in., and at the bottom 104 in. by 18 in. This tapering of the retort provides against the danger of any wedging or jamming on the part of the coal as it is turned to coke on the way down.

PRODUCER GAS

The walls of the retort enclose passages through which the heating flames pass, and Fig. 4 shows the ovens that make the gas to provide this heat. Before the company can make the gas they are to sell, they have to make some which will roast the coal. The reader may ask why this heating gas cannot be sold direct and so save further trouble, but the answer to that is laid down in an Act of Parliament. Gas as sold to consumers, as we have seen already, must conform to certain minimum standards of

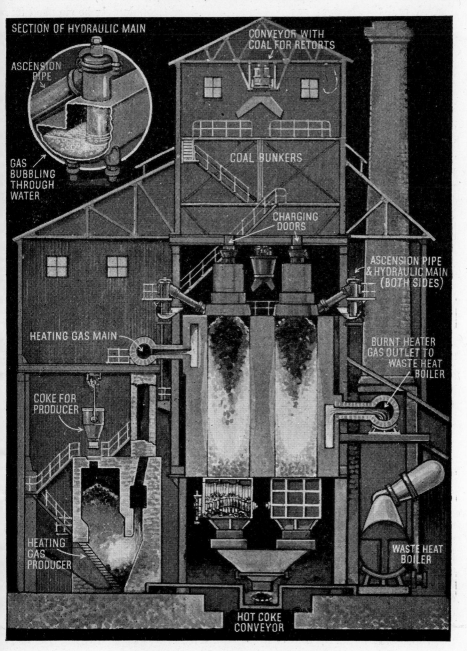

SECTION OF HYDRAULIC MAIN

ASCENSION PIPE

GAS BUBBLING THROUGH WATER

CONVEYOR WITH COAL FOR RETORTS

COAL BUNKERS

CHARGING DOORS

ASCENSION PIPE & HYDRAULIC MAIN (BOTH SIDES)

HEATING GAS MAIN

BURNT HEATER GAS OUTLET TO WASTE HEAT BOILER

COKE FOR PRODUCER

HEATING GAS PRODUCER

WASTE HEAT BOILER

HOT COKE CONVEYOR

MODERN VERTICAL RETORT HOUSE

Fig. 4. *In this type of retort house, shown above in section, the coal is lifted to bunkers at the top by means of continuously running conveyors. The retorts are heated by gas from the producer plant below, using already expended coke from the retorts.*

E.T.T.S.—E

quality, and this heating gas falls far short of that necessary standard.

Moreover, it has another disadvantage: it is what the engineer calls producer gas, and is made from coke, one of the by-products from the retorts.

This gas is made in an oven that burns coke with only a very small quantity of air, insufficient, in fact, to burn it properly. Those with some knowledge of chemistry will recognise that the product is carbon monoxide, a gas con-

odourless it could never be supplied for public use without some addition to enable it to be easily identified and its dangers guarded against. It does the work of heating the gas-making retorts, and was formerly employed in industry for driving gas-engines. It would not serve very well in the domestic cooker, as in the small quantities needed for domestic use its heating value is poor.

A section of a pair of vertical retorts is shown in Fig. 4. Various arrange-

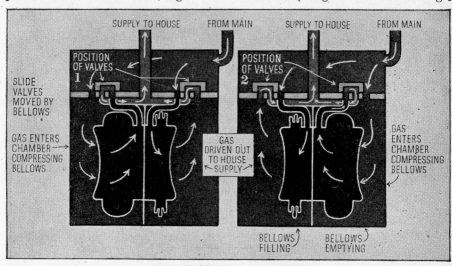

THE DOMESTIC GAS METER

Fig. 5. *At* 1, *the slide valve—an inverted box connecting two of the three holes—is allowing gas to enter the outer chamber from the main, thus compressing the leather bellows and driving the gas in them to the oven. In position 2, gas entering the bellows drives that in the outer chamber to the oven. Doubling the bellows gives greater capacity.*

sisting of molecules each containing one atom of carbon with only one accompanying atom of oxygen. Only enough air to burn the coke at the bottom of the stove is admitted, and this produces carbon dioxide, the full product of combustion. This gas has to escape through the mass of heated coke above, the carbon atoms from the coke combine with it, and carbon monoxide results.

Now this gas burns with an intensely hot flame when air is available, but it is asphyxiating, and as it is colourless and

ments are in use, but the principle is more or less the same in all of them. The coal is stored in bunkers above, and when more has to be added to the retort, some precaution must be taken to prevent the gas in the retort from escaping. So a supply of coal falls into a container with sliding doors set above each retort, the upper door being closed before the lower one is opened, permitting coal to fall in slowly. Here it will yield up its gas content, and will fall as coke to the bottom of the retort,

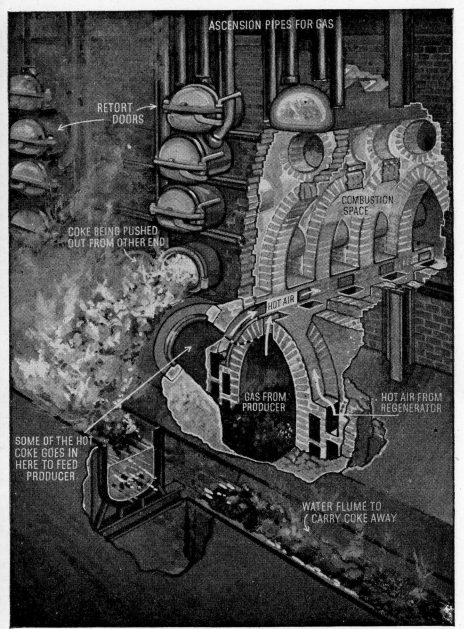

ASCENSION PIPES FOR GAS

RETORT DOORS

COMBUSTION SPACE

COKE BEING PUSHED OUT FROM OTHER END

HOT AIR

GAS FROM PRODUCER

HOT AIR FROM REGENERATOR

SOME OF THE HOT COKE GOES IN HERE TO FEED PRODUCER

WATER FLUME TO CARRY COKE AWAY

CONSTRUCTION OF A HORIZONTAL RETORT

Fig. 6. *A bank of horizontal retorts broken away to show interior construction. One retort door is opened, showing the expended coke being driven out from the other end after the gas has been made. A water flume quenches the coke and carries away what has not been used up for the gas to feed the producer gas plant below, which in turn heats the retort.*

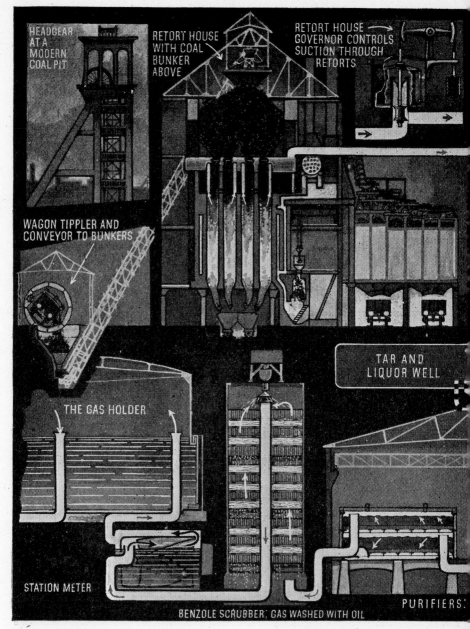

STAGES IN GAS PRODUCTION

Fig. 7. *Diagram to show the processes from raw coal from the colliery to the gasholder.*
The broad white band with arrows traces the path of the gas, drawn out of the retort
by the exhauster which then drives it onwards through various devices for removing
the valuable by-products. The dotted lines show the stages at which tar and ammonia

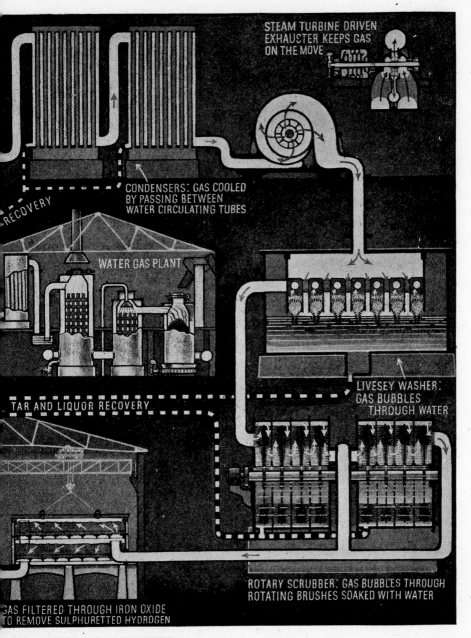

STEAM TURBINE DRIVEN
EXHAUSTER KEEPS GAS
ON THE MOVE

CONDENSERS: GAS COOLED
BY PASSING BETWEEN
WATER CIRCULATING TUBES

RECOVERY

WATER GAS PLANT

LIVESEY WASHER:
GAS BUBBLES
THROUGH WATER

TAR AND LIQUOR RECOVERY

ROTARY SCRUBBER: GAS BUBBLES THROUGH
ROTATING BRUSHES SOAKED WITH WATER

GAS FILTERED THROUGH IRON OXIDE
TO REMOVE SULPHURETTED HYDROGEN

FROM MINE TO GASHOLDER

*are extracted. Water gas may be added at the point shown, to adjust the calorific value
of the gas, or to deal with extra heavy calls from consumers. Although water gas has less
heating value than genuine coal gas, it can be made very quickly, and its use allows
the economical production of the mixture of gases supplied as "coal gas" to the consumer.*

where, by means of a helical screw, it is carried away to a cooling chamber.

In another form of vertical retort, a gallery is built all along the tops of the retorts, which are covered by heavy iron lids. A rail track spans the lids, and on this track runs a skip, taking about three tons of coal. When the retort is to be charged, the lid is lifted, and the skip travels along and dumps its charge into the open mouth. A great cloud of yellowish smoke pours out and up, then as suddenly bursts into flame; this is the gas as it first appears. Down goes the iron lid, to remain closed till the next charging in several hours' time.

Modern gas-making practice favours the admission of a certain amount of steam at the bottom of the retort. The result of the passage of this vapour through the hot coke inside is to decompose it, producing carbon monoxide and hydrogen, known as blue water gas. The heating value of this gas is much lower than that of coal gas, but by moderate steaming the total gas yielded by a ton of coal can be increased by about 40 per cent, though its value drops to 460 B.Th.U. per cubic foot.

HORIZONTAL RETORTS

Though the vertical retort is now preferred by the gas engineer, a large volume of gas is still produced in horizontal retorts (Fig. 6) consisting of horizontal ovens about 20 feet long with doors at each end, and outlet pipes rising from them to the collecting main. These ovens are built in blocks of up to ten (Fig. 8), and are heated in a similar manner to the vertical. Charging (shown in Fig. 1) is done by a mechanically propelled carriage on a rail track which moves along to the retort which requires a fresh charge, bringing with it the necessary coal in a hopper above. The retort doors are opened, a hydraulic or other mechanically propelled ram drives

the fresh charge of coal in, pushing the coke out at the other end (Fig. 11). This is the place from which to view the operation! The flaming coke tips out into a skip, and is quickly trundled along to the cooling tower, where a measured quantity of water is poured on to it to quench it.

Coke is one of the most valuable products in gas-making; the gas company need a good deal of it themselves, and the remainder is graded for others who want it, notably the steel works.

ASCENSION PIPES

Returning now to the output of gas from the retorts. This rises by way of the ascension pipes into the hydraulic main, a large horizontal pipe running the whole length of the bench of retorts. A steady stream of water flows through it, the depth being carefully regulated. Each ascension pipe dips down into this stream, its mouth opening below the water, thus sealing each retort off from its neighbour. All the gas must bubble through the water to pass on. The idea of this is to prevent gas escaping into any retort not in immediate use.

The gas from the hydraulic main passes into the well-named foul main. It is the same yellowish smoke we have seen during the charging operation, a very far cry from the clear, invisible gas that will ultimately be delivered to the consumers. A certain amount of impurity will be left in the water of the hydraulic main, but this is all collected for treatment. The smoky appearance is due to fine particles of tar, an inevitable product when vegetable matter —and such coal is—is distilled.

The foul main carries the gas to the condensers, where it is cooled in much the same way as the cooling water of a motor-car is cooled. It passes through iron tubes surrounded by cold water or air. The tubes are so arranged that the

HORIZONTAL RETORT HOUSE

Fig. 8. *This view of a horizontal retort house shows how the retorts are built up in groups of three to ten, allowing some hundreds to be housed in a small space.*

tar, and another by-product, a liquid containing much ammonia—ammoniacal liquor as it is called—will trickle away into a large underground tank.

This tank is the tar well, and a certain amount of natural separation goes on in it, as the tar settles to the bottom. There we can leave it for the present.

Most companies add a gas known as "carburetted water gas" to the normal supply. This is not coal gas at all, but carbon monoxide with a vapour derived from oil added to it. This gas has the merit of being very quickly made, and so a sudden extra demand on the part of the public can be provided for by increasing the output from the water gas plant. It is mentioned at this stage because the output of water gas from the generators goes into the condensers with the unwashed gas from the foul main.

The process of making it consists first of blowing a strong blast of air through burning coke, whipping it up to a fierce temperature. Then the air is cut off and the blast is replaced by steam at high pressure, resulting in the disintegration of the steam, and a volume of hydrogen and carbon monoxide. This passes to the carburettor, where it circulates through open brickwork heated by the hot blast from the generator. From the top a spray of heavy oil is discharged, to be quickly vaporized, mingling with the hydrogen and carbon monoxide. The next stage is a passage through the fixing superheater, the object of which is to mix the ingredients thoroughly and prevent the oil gas from condensing back to liquid again. Fig. 10 illustrates the sequence of operations in a typical plant.

To return now to the main gas production; we left this at the condenser, where much, though not all, of the tar is extracted. It is necessary to keep the gas continuously flowing, and rotary pumps that never stop, even for years at a time, attend to this duty. These pumps, more properly called exhausters, are quite different from the ordinary idea of a pump. A section of one of them is shown in Fig. 7, from which it can be seen that the impelling parts consist of sliding vanes working eccentrically in a cylindrical casing. The effective work is done by drawing the gas into the casing and then pushing it out. The engine room, where steam engines drive these pumps, is usually one of the finest sights in the whole works. An engine that must run non-stop perhaps for years on end has to be well looked after.

From the retort house the gas passes through a governor in the foul main, the object being to maintain an even flow.

It is a simple device that varies the size of the opening, quite automatically.

After leaving the condenser the gas has to be washed, to get rid of the ammonia. Ammonia is readily soluble in water, which will pick up 900 times its own weight. The Livesey washer makes the gas bubble through water—shown in section in Fig. 7; it then escapes by way of perforated pipes, passing on to the scrubber. Here it rises through the inside of a tower about 50 feet high, divided into four compartments separated by perforated trays covered with coke. From the top a continuous shower of water pours down, absorbing the last of the ammonia; but the gas has still another adulteration, the unpleasantly smelling sulphuretted hydrogen. To get rid of this the gas passes into the purifier, where it makes contact with layers of bog iron ore. This substance has an affinity for the sulphur in the sulphuretted hydrogen, the result being

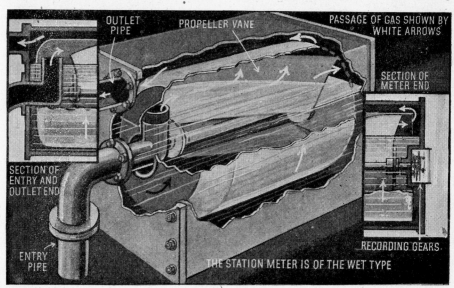

STATION METER

Fig. 9. *Gas going out of the holder passes through the station meter; its flow turns the propeller vane whose revolutions automatically record the volume passed out. The principle here is very different from that of the domestic meter, shown in Fig. 5.*

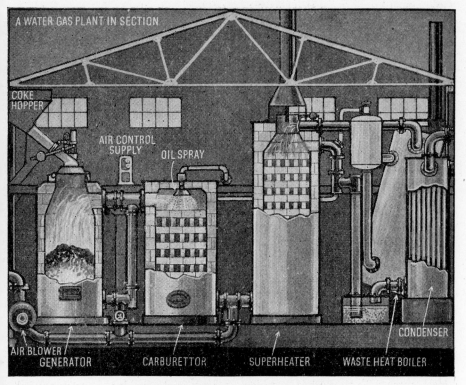

A WATER GAS PLANT IN SECTION

COKE HOPPER

AIR CONTROL SUPPLY

OIL SPRAY

CONDENSER

AIR BLOWER

GENERATOR   CARBURETTOR   SUPERHEATER   WASTE HEAT BOILER

CARBURETTED WATER GAS PLANT

Fig. 10. *Water gas is generated by blowing steam through incandescent coke. Oil vapour is added, and the mixture is then superheated to make it permanent.*

iron sulphide and water. When the iron ore has picked up as much sulphur as possible, it is spread out in the open; the oxygen in the air displaces the sulphur to some extent, and the iron oxide is refreshed. It can then be used over again, the process being repeated until it is about half sulphur. No further refreshing is then possible, and the makers of sulphuric acid take over the stuff to roast for sulphur dioxide.

Not yet can the gas be passed into the great gasholders, for there is still one more troublesome substance—naphthalene—held in suspension in it. This would, and does, deposit on the inside of the distribution pipes, clogging them in a way that is very difficult to clear.

E.T.T.S.—E*

Prussian blue, and anthracene oil, valuable in aniline dye production, can also be extracted at this stage. So, after these substances have been removed by the rotary stripping washer, the gas can now flow into the gasholders by way of the station meter (Fig. 9).

This meter is an interesting device, consisting of a set of spiral blades on a shaft, half immersed in water. The gas enters at one end, but can escape only by pressing against the blades, thus turning them round on the shaft which, by its movement, operates a train of gear wheels. By means of indicating pointers and dials the revolutions are recorded so that the volume of gas passed through is exactly known. This meter is of a quite different type from those used in the consumers' houses, which will be described shortly.

Gasholders—almost invariably called gasometers, or gas-measurers, which they are not—are of two distinct types. These are illustrated in section in Fig. 12. The older type is made up of a large bell floating in a tank of water. The tank is simply a steel cylinder built around a conical concrete dumpling, with a wide interior space for water, with which it is filled to the brim; the inlet and outlet pipes for the gas are brought in below the foundations, and their mouths are set above the water level. The bell, or "lift", when the holder is empty, rests on the foundation, but when gas is admitted its pressure lifts it, the sliding seal being made by the water picked up. A section of this seal is also shown. To make the gasholder's capacity greater additional lifts in the form of open cylinders, even up to six in number, may be added. The older types of gasholder were built with a steel frame with roller guides, which gave stability against the wind when the lifts were extended. The weight of the lifts provides the pressure needed to drive the gas out and into the mains.

MODERN GASHOLDERS

The more modern type of gasholder consists of a permanent cylindrical outer structure, with a piston sliding inside it. The ring of contact between the piston and the housing is kept gastight by the use of tar in an interesting manner, illustrated in section. There is not much difficulty in understanding the action of this type, illustrated in Fig. 12. Yet another type, used for holding gas at high pressure, is shown in Fig. 2.

Many towns now depend for their gas supply on a works situated at some distance, perhaps as much as fifteen miles away, too far for unassisted dis-

tribution at ordinary pressure. A gasholder will be built in the town, but the gas to fill it will have to be at a much higher pressure than the normal. This involves the use of steel mains with welded joints, and pumping will have to be resorted to in order to overcome the resistance of the long pipe. Fig. 7 shows a section of a "booster" used for this purpose driven by a steam turbine.

REGULATING PRESSURE

In order to exercise some control over the gas pressure in the mains, and to prevent it from rising to a point that might be dangerous, a governor is inserted outside the gasholder on the outlet main. This is a simple arrangement by which the incoming gas passes through a conical valve suspended from a bell floating in water, the interior of the bell being open to the gas. If the pressure rises the bell is lifted and the valve closed a little, checking the flow to the main. A fine-bore tube connects the interior of the bell with the main pipe, to enable the gas in the bell to leak away slowly; otherwise it might hold the valve continuously shut.

The meter that counts up the cubic feet in your house is an ingenious piece of work, a mechanical and pneumatic arrangement that will do its duty for years without the slightest attention. A glance at Fig. 5, which shows the principle on which they all work, should explain the idea. Gas from the main flows into the bellows and the outer chamber alternately, admission to either side being controlled by a slide valve which is knocked from side to side by the action of the bellows as it fills and is emptied. The gas leaving the bellows or the outer chamber flows into the service pipe of the house, being pumped out by the pressure of the gas coming in from the main. The slide valve is an ingenious contrivance, consisting of a hollow box,

DISCHARGING COKE FROM A HORIZONTAL RETORT

Fig. 11. *The photograph gives some idea of the spectacular effect of this operation. Flaming coke is pouring into the skip below, while the fresh charge is being rammed into the retort at the opposite end. Power-driven rams—usually operated electrically by reason of the simplicity with which they can be controlled—perform both operations. Twelve hours must be allowed for coal to become carbonised, at the end of which time the discharging and refuelling takes place. The hot and exhausted coke is then guided away into a trough, where it is cooled under a cascade of water whose volume is automatically controlled.*

sliding over three holes and able to cover two of them at a time. The middle hole opens into the house service pipe, and the two outer ones to the bellows and the outer chamber. When the valve is pushed one way it connects the bellows with the service pipe and opens the outer chamber to the main supply; gas flows through and flattens the bellows, driving the gas out into the service pipe. At the end of the bellows' movement it knocks the valve over the opposite way, so opening the outer chamber to the service pipe and the bellows to the main; as soon as the bellows have filled, the valve is knocked over again. The meter has two separate compartments in each of which this sequence goes on.

And that is not only how gas is made, but also how it is delivered to you, a clean, efficient fuel, a very far cry from the questionable smoky stuff our grandfathers had to use. Fig. 7 shows the whole process, from colliery to gasholder.

As a postscript, here are some details of what the Gas Company get from a ton of coal. A good quality of gas-making coal should produce:

Gas—14,000 cubic feet—or say 70 therms; Tar—9–11 gallons; Ammoniacal Liquor—about 35 gallons; Sulphate of Ammonia—25 lb.; Sulphur—5–7 lb.; Cyanogen—4 lb.; Coke and Breeze—approximately 13 hundredweight.

TWO TYPES OF GASHOLDER

Fig. 12. *Two of the gasholders in general use are shown above. That on the left has a piston sealed by gas tar, in a fixed cylinder; the other has a series of lifts with a top bell, sealed by water. The former type is the one in more general use.*

CANNED FOOD

Value of Preserved Food. Drying and Freezing. Tinplate and its Manufacture.
Modern Methods. Tinning the Plates. Lacquering Processes. Canning Beer.
Fruits and Vegetables. Cooking and Cooling.

THE utility and value of preserved food has been vividly brought home to us in recent times by the events of the Second World War. It was, indeed, in a sense due to a former War Lord and dictator that the art of preserving food in metal containers was born, and began that path of progress which has brought it to the important position it holds in civilised communities today. It was Napoleon Bonaparte who offered a handsome prize to the man who could preserve meat and put it up in portable form for easy transport. The name of Nicholas Appert, the prize-winner, means little to any of us, but who is there who has not heard of "bully" beef, which is simply the "bouilli" of Napoleon's soldiery?

The main problem that has to be faced in connection with food preservation is the immediate tendency of fresh foods to begin fermentation. This, as has long been recognised, is due to the action of various bacteria. These bacteria can be destroyed, but unless the destroying agency is kept active, the mischief starts again at once.

OLD-FASHIONED PRESERVATIVES

In olden days the sailor on a long voyage took his meat supplies to sea with him well salted, for the bacteria do not care for salt and will keep away from it, but the meat lost much of its palatability and much of it was wasted.

Drying was another process employed: ferments cannot get to work unless there is some degree of moisture in the food. Smoking was also used, as it still is today, especially for fish. Chemical substances deposited upon the fish by the smoke aided preservation and, incidentally, improved the flavour.

Again, freezing or chilling arrests all fermentation and action by bacteria; this fact has proved a great boon to the population of the British Isles because it has made possible the importation of vast quantities of meat and fruit that would be otherwise unobtainable. None of these methods, however, is practicable for the preservation and storage of food in places where no special facilities are available, as in the home.

BACTERIA MUST BE DESTROYED

It is well known that heat will destroy bacteria and, also, that fermentation will not take place where free oxygen is not present. So the ideal that the canner sets out to achieve is a vessel containing the food, sealed hermetically against the entry of liquid or air, inside which he has been able to create a complete or partial vacuum.

First of all, the container must be considered; of what must it be composed—how cheaply can it be made? Fortunately the answer is easy. Tin plate—which is really steel plate coated with a thin film of tin on both sides—was already an old invention by Nicholas Appert's time; it was an eminently suitable material possessing all the properties required. It was easy to work it into the bent and folded shapes needed and, even more important, its tin coating resisted attack by the acids which many foods contain.

A modern tinplate mill can show machinery of the most massive description. There are actually two processes in general use, though in both of them the plates are rolled. The first stage is the steel ingot, a heavy billet that may tip the scale at 5 tons. This is brought to white heat in a soaking pit—a kind of upright furnace—and when ready is lifted out and carried by travelling crane to the cogging rolls. This massive machine somewhat resembles a vast mangle with uneven rollers between which the ingot passes several times.

ROLLING THE STEEL

Sprays of water directed against it break off the oxide scale and it goes forward on rollers, propelled by the inexorable pressure of hydraulic pushers. Once between the rollers it is very quickly reduced to a slab and its length considerably increased. The slab is sheared into smaller pieces; these go through other sets of rollers to be brought to a standard shape known as a tinplate bar, about 40 in. long, 8 in. wide and $\frac{3}{8}$ in. thick. Ductility will have been imparted to the steel by this and subsequent rollings (Fig. 2).

Two of these bars are re-heated and run together through the mill, bringing their width to about 20 in. and then, by rolling once more, to a length of 60 in. They are next doubled, so as to present two folded sheets 20 × 30 in., and another passage through the rolls brings the length to 84 in. The next operation is to shear them into three packs of four sheets, 20 × 28 in. In this state they go to the pickling bath, the "black" pickle, of weak sulphuric acid at boiling point. The acid is then washed off and a process of annealing at a temperature of 1500°–1800° F. in an oven from which air is excluded takes place. This is continued for about 24 hours, during which they are heated up slowly,

soaked in the heat and allowed slowly to cool. Next they will be rolled cold between highly polished rolls; a second pickling follows—the "white" pickle. Stacked in weak acid water, they now await the stage when the coating of tin will be added (Fig. 3).

This time-honoured method of producing tinplates is known as pack rolling. But there is now another method, developed as a result of the great demand for thin steel plate and strip by motor-car and aircraft manufacturers. Much has been heard in recent years of the new continuous rolling mills set up in South Wales, to roll strip steel for this purpose. In mills similar to these a continuous length, up to 2,000 feet, of tinplate sheet can be rolled. From the hot ingot a strip is rolled to $\frac{1}{16}$ inch thickness at something like 20 miles an hour. After this, the strip is rolled cold down to the required thickness, cut up to size, pickled and annealed as in the previous process. Tinning is carried out by feeding the sheets, by pairs of rollers, through baths of molten tin which is maintained in that state by gas flames below.

TINNING PROCESS

The sheets, which lie in a trough of water awaiting their turn, are picked up and fed into the first set of rollers. This carries them through a pool of zinc chloride floating on top of the tin, the object of which is to flux the sheet to enable it to take the tin properly. Straight on through the molten tin it goes, picking up a film on both sides, then up and out for inspection; then down once more through a second tin bath. It comes out of this through a compartment filled with palm oil, which cools it. The rollers here are adjusted to squeeze off any excess of tin from the sheets. A normal tin coating will be something less than $\frac{1}{1000}$ inch thick,

FILLING AND SEALING CANS OF BEER

Fig. 1. *Beer is canned in Great Britain mainly for export. The tins have to be stronger than usual, owing to the greater pressures caused by the pasteurizing process.*

and a box of 112 plates 20 in. × 14 in. will have used up no more than 2 or 3 lb. of tin altogether.

Having made the tinned sheet, the next thing is to make a tin—or can, as it is more generally called nowadays. Most cans are cylindrical; though other shapes are still employed; this shape has numerous advantages—for transport— it will roll and travel by its own weight. The usual type of can is described as sanitary, as it requires no solder inside.

Rectangular pieces for the body are quickly cut by "slitters", the corners are notched and the edges hooked. They are bent over a cylindrical mandrel to their final shape, the hooks engaged, flattened, and given a smear of flux; a quick dip in molten solder seals

up and locks the outside seam. All this happens in less time than it takes to read the description.

Any excess of solder is rubbed off with a buffing wheel and a jet of air quickly cools it. The body then passes to a machine that turns down a flange on the rim, top and bottom. Disks for the lids are stamped from similar sheets; these are simultaneously impressed with the necessary corrugations for stiffness, a downward curl being given to the edge to prevent any tendency to nest together when they are stacked. A thin layer of rubber sealing solution is run round under the curled edge—the volatile spirit in this being baked out in a quick run through an oven—and the bottom meets its can body (Fig. 4).

POURING LIQUID STEEL INTO INGOT MOULDS

STRIPPING MOULDS FROM HOT INGOTS

THE PLUG IN THE CRUCIBLE

POWER SCREW ADJUSTMENT FOR CLEARANCE BETWEEN ROLLS

TOGGLE FOR LIFTING HOT INGOTS BY CRANE

WATER JETS TO BREAK OFF SCALE

HAND SCREW ADJUSTMENT FOR ROLLS

DRIVING SHAFT

TOP ROLL

BOTTOM ROLL

TOP ROLL

INGOT ON ROLLERS

ROLLERS ON WHICH INGOT TRAVELS

A COGGING MILL REDUCING AN INGOT TO SMALLER SIZE BARS OR BLOOMS

SMALLER ROLLING MILL FOR PRODUCING TINPLATE BARS

PROCESSES IN THE MAKING OF TIN PLATE

Fig. 2. *Tin plate is made from mild steel ingots. The ingots are first cast in simple moulds, then rolled under pressure whilst still malleable into bars of smaller size. Repeated rollings gives ductility or flexibility to the steel, a most important and desirable quality.*

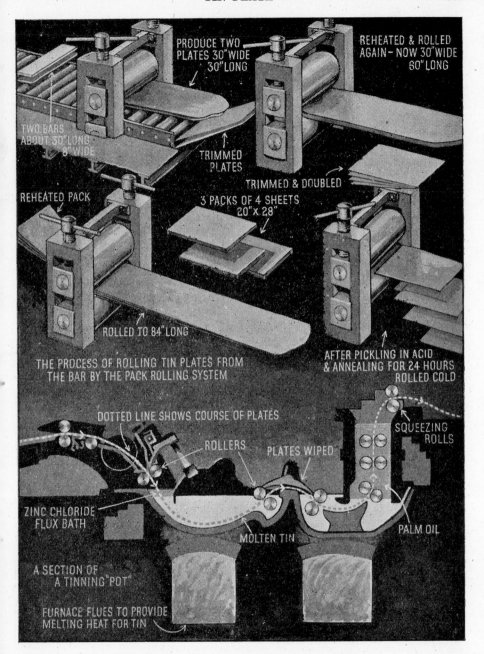

PRODUCE TWO PLATES 30"WIDE 30"LONG

REHEATED & ROLLED AGAIN – NOW 30"WIDE 60"LONG

TWO BARS ABOUT 30"LONG 8" WIDE

TRIMMED PLATES

TRIMMED & DOUBLED

REHEATED PACK

3 PACKS OF 4 SHEETS 20"x 28"

ROLLED TO 84"LONG

THE PROCESS OF ROLLING TIN PLATES FROM THE BAR BY THE PACK ROLLING SYSTEM

AFTER PICKLING IN ACID & ANNEALING FOR 24 HOURS ROLLED COLD

DOTTED LINE SHOWS COURSE OF PLATES

ROLLERS

PLATES WIPED

SQUEEZING ROLLS

ZINC CHLORIDE FLUX BATH

MOLTEN TIN

PALM OIL

A SECTION OF A TINNING "POT"

FURNACE FLUES TO PROVIDE MELTING HEAT FOR TIN

HOW THE BARS ARE ROLLED INTO SHEETS

Fig. 3. *Simplified diagram of the pack-rolling system. Below is a sectional view of the tinning bath, in which the sheets receive their protective coating of pure tin. This coating is so fine that it is frequently less than one-thousandth of an inch thick.*

The double seaming process, which is completed in two stages, is designed to seal the container hermetically against leakage in or out. The first roll curls the edges together, and the second tightens the seam. This part of the work is now thoroughly tested under pressure. First, the open end of the can having been clamped tightly on to a rubber pad, compressed air is blown in by way of a pipe through the pad; any leakage of air is noted instantly by a detector and the can discarded. Next, the air from the can is exhausted and a pressure of 10 lb. to the square inch applied outside it. Any failure is at once recorded, and the faulty can rejected; but failures are quite uncommon and the approved cans come rolling out of the machine as quickly as they can be counted.

There is now a preference for lacquered interiors to the cans as these provide an additional guarantee against possible corrosion by fruit acids. Statistics give the fullest details as to this corrosion; every fish, meat, fruit, or vegetable that has ever been canned (there are more than 300 of them) and every one that has ever been considered for canning has its pigeon-hole in the records. Everything, down to the last detail, is known about every one of them, what they will do and how any mischievous activities have, if possible, been successfully combated.

In some cases the tinned sheets are lacquered before being made up, the lacquer used being flexible when dry and able to stand up to the tight folding and creasing. A more customary method is to fill the can with lacquer, then pour it off and drain it with a spinning motion to make quite sure that it adequately covers the fine crevices of the interior seams. Yet another scheme under trial makes use of a pressure spray to coat the inside of the can.

Not all lacquers, of course, are called upon to resist fruit juices. Certain vegetables tended to emit sulphur,

EXAMINING COOKED PEAS ON THE CONVEYOR BELT

Although peas can be handled throughout the process entirely by canning machinery, the final decision as to quality still rests with the individual operative.

IN THE PACKING ROOM

Cases of peas being packed for transport after the tins leave the cooking tank. Green peas are by far the most commonly canned vegetable in England and fixing the colour so that it will remain bright green is regarded as a most important process.

which blackened the surface of the tin, and though this did no particular harm, it caused an appearance unattractive to the housewife, who was at one time faintly suspicious of canned vegetables. It had therefore to be eliminated, and coating the interior of the tins with a suitable lacquer has been found the simplest and most efficient method.

Beer is now canned extensively for export (Fig. 1), though the idea has not yet caught on in Britain for home consumption. The cans for beer have to be of stouter construction, as the pasteurizing process tends to set up considerable pressure inside. Wax of some kind is often used in beer cans in place of lacquer.

Each class of product may call for a different kind of lacquer, and formulas

for all these have been worked out and tested most rigorously. It is this painstaking research that is largely responsible for the vast increase in the consumption of canned goods and of public confidence in them.

FRUIT CANNING

The can being made and ready, it is washed, dried and put on the conveyor belt to join the never-ending procession to the filling machines. Different products require different treatment and there is not the space to deal with all; here, therefore, we will consider fruit canning only.

Peaches are certainly in normal times the favourite fruit for canning. Most of them come from California, where vast quantities are grown. Pineapples run peaches pretty close in the race for popularity, so it is fortunate that both these fruits lend themselves particularly well to canning. Peaches are cut open and the stones—"pits", as the canners call them—removed. The cutting may be done either by hand or by machine that saws the fruit in halves, pit and all, the two halves of the pit being then cut out by hand. The skins are removed by spraying with a hot, weak solution of caustic soda, and a thorough washing follows this process.

SLICING FRUIT BY MACHINE

If sliced fruit is wanted, slicing is also done in a machine. The removal of the pits is carried out in various ways for other fruits, some of which are canned whole, in which case—as with plums, cherries and others—the pit is pushed out with a punching movement, likewise in a machine. The multiplicity and ingenuity of such machines in a large factory pass belief, and are a testimony to the skill of the inventor and the machine builder. Apricots are usually canned with their skins on and their pits in, so washing is the only process, apart from thorough inspection, which is applied to this favourite fruit.

PINEAPPLE CANNING

Pineapples are mostly handled by the Ginaca machine. This cuts off the ends, and sizes them to the correct diameter to enter the can, removing the outer shell. Owing to the nature of the acid juice of this fruit, the girls who inspect them as they come on to the tables have to wear rubber gloves; these girls cut out all spots and blemishes before washing. Cutting up into the various forms, slices, cubes, and so on, is a mechanically performed job. The syrup added to the fruit is made from the waste discharged from the Ginaca machine, which is first of all

crushed and filtered, and then subjected to a certain amount of dilution.

Some of the smaller fruits, such as blackberries, raspberries and loganberries, which cannot be processed owing to their nature, are thoroughly inspected and then canned with the greatest expedition in order to ensure the utmost perfection. Gooseberries can be put through a machine to top and tail them; in some cases even the excess hairs may be singed off.

In England green peas are by far the most commonly canned of all fruits or vegetables (Fig. 5). Ingenious machinery has been devised for handling and grading them. The viner goes out into the fields, where the plants are rooted up and pitchforked into its hopper. The waste, stems and leaves having been thrown out, the peas are extracted from their shells and graded as to size; they are then delivered into tubs ready for transport to the canning factory.

FIXING THE COLOUR OF PEAS

Here they are again graded, those that harbour maggots are discarded and any with grub-holes are caught on little hooks and similarly dealt with. Yet another machine takes them by way of a spiral conveyor through a bath of boiling water for a period not exceeding half a minute. This blanches them and fixes the colour, a most important point, for "pea green" is a most attractive colour on the table.

Though it does not come in the same category as fruit, a word on the subject of milk may be added. It is evaporated in a vacuum of 29 inches, as high a degree as is commercially possible, at a temperature of 145° F., being kept on the move continuously by a mechanical paddle or impeller. This process is followed in turn by the three processes of homogenizing, filtering and cooling. We must now return to the can,

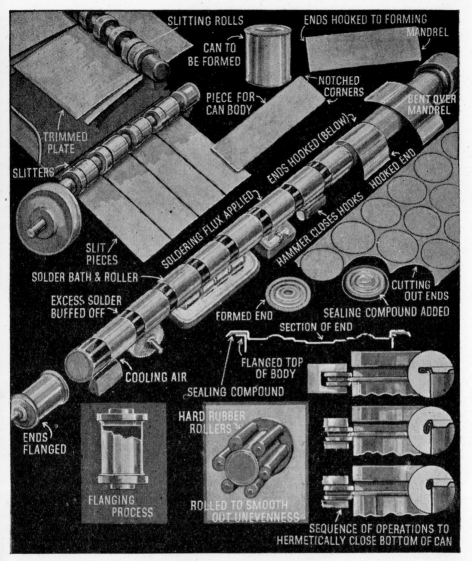

MASS PRODUCTION OF CANS

Fig. 4. *Can bodies are formed on a mandrel, along which they move to receive each successive operation. When the base is rolled on the can is ready for filling or lacquering.*

waiting at the filling platform, having come down a long conveyor chute, with hundreds more behind it. The washed and blanched fruit is in a big hopper tank, from which it is measured and shot into the can by way of one of a series of spouts. Round goes the can in a circular track, passing to the syruping machine for the addition of sugar and water, brine, soup, or whatever the accompanying fluid is to be. This process is quite a critical affair, for a

THE VINER TAKES THE WHOLE PLANT ROOTED FROM THE FIELD AND THRASHES THE PEAS FROM IT

BEATER DRUMS

PEAS TO CANNING FACTORY

WASTE CHUTE

DELIVERY CONVEYOR

LIDS PUT ON & LIGHTLY SEAMED

LID PUT ON LIGHTLY SEAMED

BRINE ADDED

FILLED CAN FROM FILLER

FILLING MACHINE

HEAD SPACE

DOUBLE SEAMING THE CA

GEARED DISCS CARRYING CANS THROUGH THE EXHAUSTER FOR SIX MINUTES AT 180° FAHR.

GREEN PEAS GATHERED IN THE FIELD CAN BE

Fig. 5. *A pictorial diagram of the whole process from start to finish. The peas are shelled, washed, graded, blanched, canned and cooked entirely by machinery. Sorting the good from the bad is the only operation which has to be performed by hand. Top left shows peas, stems and*

HING MACHINE

WATER WHEEL RETURNS WATER TO HOPPER

CLOVERLEAF ROTATING PEA GRADER

WATER SPRAYS IN HERE

LE BOARD

FEED HOPPER

DELIVERY CHUTE

FEED HOPPER

METAL SCREENS

CHUTE FOR RUBBISH

RAL CONVEYOR

DELIVERY CHUTES

LARGE

MEDIUM

SMALL

CHILLED BY COLD SPRAYS

HAND PICKING TABLE

BLANCHING PROCESS ½ MIN. IN BOILING WATER FIXES COLOUR

CONVEYOR BELT

CONVEYOR TO COOLER

OUTLET AFTER 35 MINUTES AT 240° FAHR.

EYOR

ENTRY VALVE INTO RETORT

READY IN TINS IN LITTLE OVER AN HOUR

roots included, arriving at the factory, whilst at bottom right the tins are ready for packing. The whole canning process is so rapid that in considerably less than an hour from their arrival at the factory gates from the field the peas can, if necessary, be served for lunch.

reason that will soon be made plain. The contents are pressed down to a predetermined level in the can, and the syrup added to reach a definite level also, thus leaving a fixed space at the top called the "head space". In a normal can this head space is about ⅛-inch when the lid is put on. As a rule, the syrup filling is put into the cans at as high a temperature as possible.

EXHAUSTING

Now the lid is put on, and sealed up; not so tightly that air or steam cannot escape during the next process, that of exhausting, but tightly enough to prevent leakage of the contents (Fig. 6).

The idea of exhausting is to drive out all the air in the can and to replace it with steam. When the contents cool, the steam condenses, leaving a partial vacuum in the head space. To do this, the cans are stood up in hot water, maintained at about 180° F., to within an inch of their tops; they are then carried on conveyors designed to transport them in a roundabout path through the tank, on horizontal disks, being steered from one to the other by guide bars. Six minutes is considered long enough. Vegetables may be treated by playing jets of steam on the tops and sides of the cans for about one minute.

STERILISATION

The lids must now be quickly and tightly seamed on to prevent entry of air, and there is a machine in which this tightening is done under vacuum.

Now the product is fairly and truly sealed up, but it is by no means yet ready to go out. The most important stage is now reached, that of sterilisation, more commonly called retorting, the purpose of which is to destroy the bacteria inevitably present. As a result of much experiment the precise temperatures necessary to effect this with every product, without risking any damage to the contents, has been discovered; the research men call these temperatures the "thermal death-times of food-spoiling organisms". For most vegetables the temperature is about 232° F., for evaporated milk it is about 242° and for meat 246°.

It is not enough to submit the cans to this degree of heat for a time and hope for the best. The heat must penetrate and reach the innermost part of the contents, which does not happen so quickly as might be imagined. The cans are packed in open boilers, called retorts, and space is allowed all round for steam to circulate; the lids are secured with bolts. The times that are necessary for this process, which must be thorough, can be gauged from the fact that a liquid, such as soup, takes at least 45 minutes whereas a solid pack, such as meat, would need perhaps 105 minutes before it was really sterile.

FINAL PROCESSES

Immediately after this process the cans have to be cooled as suddenly as possible by sprays or by immersion in cold running water. Properly speaking, the canning is now completed, but a sequence of tests has still to be gone through to make sure that no undue distortion has taken place during the various processes, nor any undue pressure of gas set up inside. The most usual cause of this is an emission of hydrogen, due to a possible fault in the coating enabling fruit acid to get at the steel. This produces an easily distinguishable swelling in the can, called a hydrogen swell, generally as a result of unduly long storage. While the canners would not issue a can of any of their products in this state, there is not necessarily any question of scrapping as far as the housewife is concerned if she should find a tin in this condition.

FILLING AND SEALING ON ONE MACHINE

Fig. 6. *Filling the can with the juice or soup which is to accompany its fruit or vegetable contents is a critical operation in view of the exact level required.*

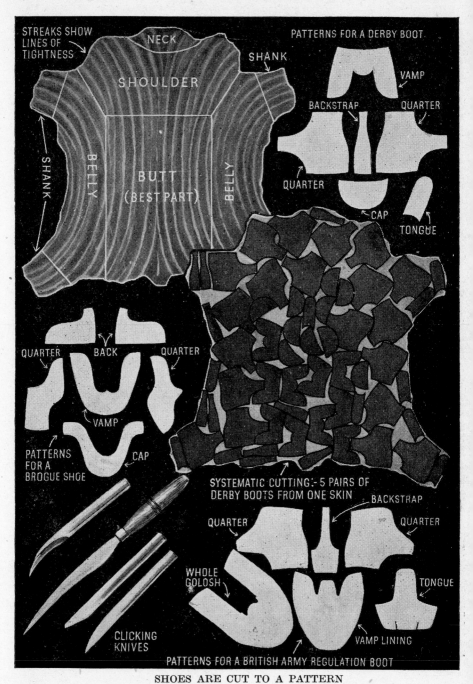

SHOES ARE CUT TO A PATTERN

Fig. 1. *Above: the parts of a whole skin as cured for footwear manufacture. Centre: a carefully planned skin, showing maximum economy, giving 10 sets of boot uppers.*

BOOTS AND SHOES

*Every Shoe Made to Measure. Scientific Footwear Principles. The Last.
Cutting to Pattern. Clicking. Skiving and Closing. Putting on the Soles. The
Veldtschoen Process. Cleaning and Trimming. Staining, Waxing and Polishing.*

How many pairs of footwear are "got through" by each one of us who attains the normal span of life? It would be hard to say. Most of us own a well-tried pair of shoes that have served well for many years and look on them as friends indeed; for that a good pair of shoes are a friend, their fortunate owners need no reminder. But it can safely be said that few of us realise the art and skill that go into their making. Even the cheapest footwear, albeit a mass-produced commodity, represents a very remarkable modern development of a highly skilled industry.

MAKING TO MEASURE

At one time, before large-scale production was thought of, the hand-made boots and shoes held the field so far as better-class footwear was concerned. The artisan and poorer classes had to be satisfied with roughly made clogs with soles of wood; the upper classes, who disdained such wear, made work for the highly-skilled shoemaker's trade; for highly-skilled trade it is. The tailor takes his measurements, cuts out odd shapes in cloth and, joining these unlikely-looking pieces together, makes you a suit that fits you to perfection. The shoemaker's job is exactly similar, but his working material is not so amenable; it has to be moulded into a predetermined shape based on years of experience and intimate knowledge of the action of the foot in walking.

It is a great mistake to imagine that a comfortable shoe will fit the foot as a glove would the hand. It certainly ought

not to do so, for if it did, no room would be provided for the movement of the complex system of joints, each of which plays its part in correct walking. And there is no necessity to "stretch" a new pair of shoes in order to make them comfortable in wear; if they have been well fitted at first, according to true principles, they should need very little use before their owner is no longer aware of their presence.

It should be understood, however, that there is some difference between the action of one pair of feet and another. Consider the footwear required, for instance, by people of different occupations. Some are on their feet all day, but of these some are standing still, others walking the city streets. Yet again there are those whose employment takes them up and down steep hillsides or over rough moorland with never a sight of a road. Each needs a stoutly made, heavy-soled boot; each has special needs that must be met. Compare the requirements of an engine-driver, a policeman or a shepherd with those of the dancer or the elegantly-shod lady who trots around the town with the least possible thickness of leather between her feet and the pavement.

FOOT STATISTICS

No matter what anyone's requirements in footwear may be, they can be accommodated, because a vast mass of statistical information, dealing with every possible need, is now available to the footwear industry. Britain's footwear industry is the best in the world, and the

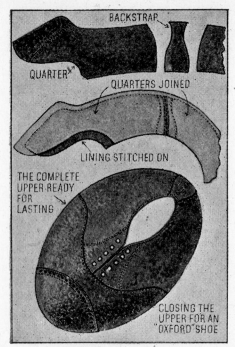

THE OXFORD SHOE

Fig. 2. *The stages in making up the upper for an Oxford type shoe are shown above.*

credit for this state of affairs goes chiefly to the British Boot, Shoe and Allied Trades Research Association. As a result of its work, a simple and convenient method of gauging the enormous variety of feet possessed by the world's population has been evolved. It is a fact that, by making two or three measurements with a simple apparatus, anyone's foot can be classified and lasts quite easily made that will guarantee comfort in footwear of any style.

This brings us to the first essential in the manufacture of footwear by whatever method—the last. Every shoe is made on a last, and the same foot needs a different pair of lasts for every different type of footwear.

Look at Fig. 8. Here we have, in diagram form, the essentials of the Association's measurement system. The foot is lightly clipped between two hinged plates that measure the angle which is suggested by its plan. This is called the focal angle. Next, the length is measured and, finally, the position of a slight bony protuberance on the outside, at the place marked E in the diagram. Having these details for each foot, the rest is easy. Though your feet might be quite unlike anyone else's in the world, to your way of thinking, yet—questions of real deformity apart —the expert needs to know nothing more about them. He can make you a pair of shoes or slippers just as you would like them.

But first he will make a pair of lasts. A last, like a horse, has points, and these are shown on the outline drawing above the foot geometry diagram (p. 161). They are the toe spring, which differs in accordance with the degree of flexibility, if any, of the sole; the waist spring, following the true shape of that part of the foot; lastly, the pitch, which allows for the height of the heel. Two drawings of lasts, one showing that for a heavy boot and another that for a light shoe, indicate the differences. As the last has to be withdrawn from the boot or shoe after manufacture is complete, it is often made with a hinged device which permits of some reduction in length so

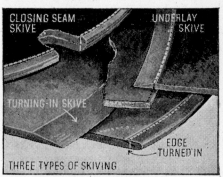

SKIVING PROCESS

Fig. 3. *Three methods of reducing or tapering the thickness of a seam.*

MACHINES FOR FOOTWEAR

Fig. 4. *Above left, clicking press; right, sewing machine; below, press for soles.*

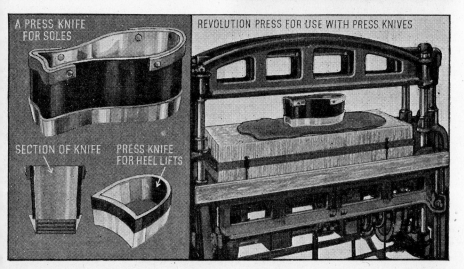

that the operator can get it out without damage to the shoe.

Now to the shoe itself. There is no need to enlarge upon the wide variety of styles. Seasonal variations and new styles have always to be provided for, but there are many standard styles that have stood the test of time.

Every style demands a different scheme of construction, involving different shapes in the cutting-out of the component pieces. Though other materials are nowadays more and more frequently employed, the most usual material is, it need hardly be said, leather; and a remarkably suitable material it is. Leather tanned in Great Britain is the finest material that can

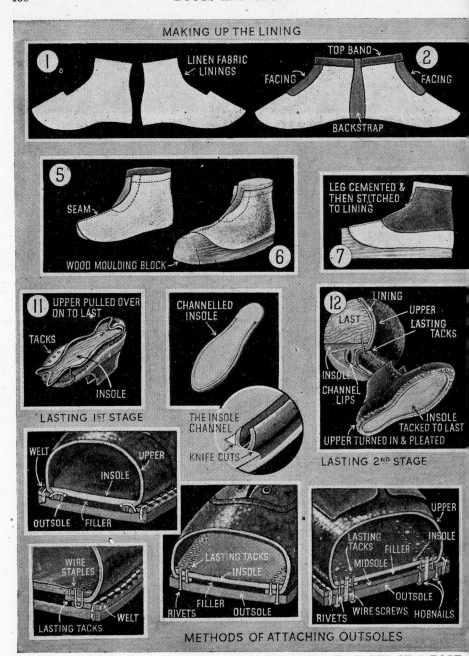

HOW THE VARIOUS PARTS OF A BOOT

Fig. 5. *The numbers in the series of drawings above indicate the sequence of manufacture of a boot of the Balmoral type. With the exception of the clicking of the pieces making up the upper, which is generally done by hand, all these*

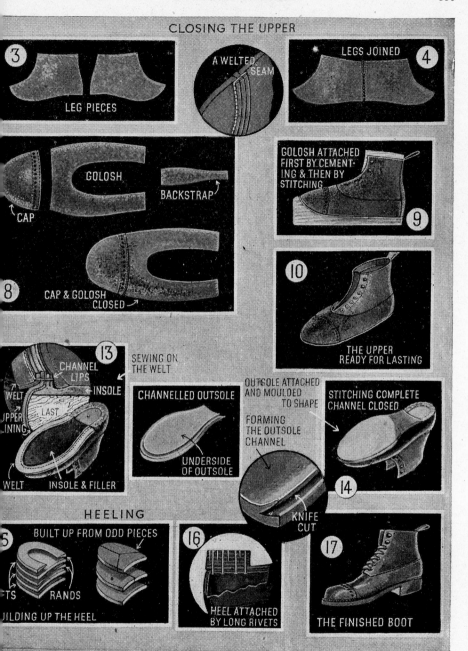

CLOSING THE UPPER

3   LEG PIECES   A WELTED SEAM   LEGS JOINED   4

GOLOSH   BACKSTRAP   CAP

GOLOSH ATTACHED FIRST BY CEMENTING & THEN BY STITCHING   9

8   CAP & GOLOSH CLOSED

10   THE UPPER READY FOR LASTING

13   CHANNEL LIPS   WELT   INSOLE   SEWING ON THE WELT

UPPER LINING   LAST   WELT   INSOLE & FILLER

CHANNELLED OUTSOLE   UNDERSIDE OF OUTSOLE

OUTSOLE ATTACHED AND MOULDED TO SHAPE   FORMING THE OUTSOLE CHANNEL   KNIFE CUT

STITCHING COMPLETE CHANNEL CLOSED   14

HEELING

15   BUILT UP FROM ODD PIECES   LIFTS   RANDS   BUILDING UP THE HEEL

16   HEEL ATTACHED BY LONG RIVETS

17   THE FINISHED BOOT

ARE CUT OUT AND FITTED TOGETHER

processes are carried out on automatic machines, some of them of amazing complexity. Clicking is the trade name for cutting out, metal patterns being used as guides, and knives of various shapes for the cutting: mechanical clicking presses are shown at Figs. 4 and 9.

be used. True, a number of substitutes have been introduced in recent years, especially rubber and similar compositions, most of them excellent, but leather remains the king of them all and is likely to continue to do so.

In Fig. 1 is outlined a typical skin and upon it are marked the names of the various parts, practically all of which can be used. The streaked effect shows the so-called "lines of tightness", in the direction of which the leather is best able to withstand stretching. The expert cutter—known as a "clicker"—must know how to arrange the patterns on the skin so as to take advantage of this property. Next is shown a skin planned out systematically to such an extent that five pairs of boot uppers can be cut from it. Also shown are three sets of patterns, a Derby boot, a brogue shoe, and a British army regulation boot.

Cutting out, or clicking, is almost entirely a hand operation, metal patterns for the desired shapes being used as guides and knives of various shapes for the cutting. The clicking board is made of blocks of wood, generally lime, set on end and clamped together. Mechanical presses are used for certain classes of work (Figs. 4 and 9).

The skill of the clicker is the beginning of a good pair of shoes, for it must be

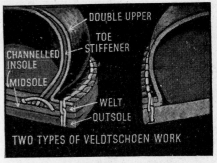

A WATERPROOF SHOE

Fig. 6. *This way of joining sole to upper is well known for its waterproof quality.*

remembered that not all leathers have a perfectly smooth surface. Skill in matching toecaps and vamps, or upper leather, so that the grain runs true from one to the other, is very necessary, even more so in the case of coloured leathers. This is accentuated where fancy material such as highly patterned lizard and snake skins are used.

When thousands of hides are dealt with, the importance of using up every inch is paramount. Each skin is measured up so that its exact area is known and, by careful arrangement, the maximum possible number of pieces will be cut from the material available.

Various systems of marking are employed by the clicker to indicate

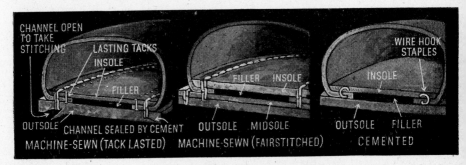

ATTACHING THE OUTER SOLE

Fig. 7. *Three more methods normally employed in fastening outsoles to uppers. Cementing, although waterproof, is usually reserved for the cheaper shoes.*

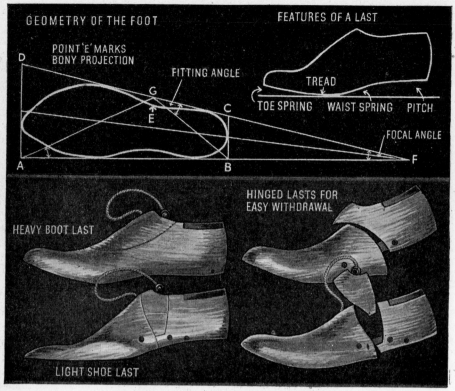

EVERY BOOT AND SHOE IS PLANNED

Fig. 8. *Every piece of footwear has to be made on a last, which is scientifically designed on geometrical principles as shown above. Various types of last are shown below.*

clearly all the details of the boot or shoe for which any given piece has been cut. This is of great importance because, though the difference between any two pieces of differing sizes is not great, it is very necessary to make sure that only those parts are mated that are designed for that purpose. Spots of coloured paint are often employed, a different colour for each standard size, or, alternatively, code letters or numbers.

Before the parts are stitched together ("closed" is the trade term) the overlapping edges must be trimmed, or "skived", to reduce their thickness. In this way high ridges that would cause discomfort to the wearer are avoided.

These skives (shown in Fig. 3) may be produced by hand or in a machine.

Few industries can claim to be more highly mechanised than the footwear trade, even though hand work plays so great a part in it. There is a machine for every operation, some of which are of a highly complex nature. Sewing machines are largely employed; these are of a variety of types, from the familiar household style to others that bear no resemblance to it whatever (Figs. 4 and 10). Two typical varieties of stitch are shown inset on Fig. 4.

The pages of drawings, Fig. 5, illustrate the processes involved in making a boot of the Balmoral type in various stages.

E.T.T.S.—F

The linings, cut from linen fabric, are first stitched together at the back, with facings of thin leather added at the tops along the fronts where the eyelets will come, and down the back. This assembly is now placed upon a shaped wooden block and, after moulding to the proper form, the front edges are seamed together. It is now ready for some of the leather parts to be added.

LEGS ARE STITCHED

The two sides, known as "legs", come first, and when these have been stitched together at the back with a cross stitch that will be flexible, and the back strap sewn on, they can be placed in position over the lining on the block. When it is certain that they fit correctly, the lining will be wiped over with some adhesive substance—usually nowadays rubber cement, though ordinary pastes are often used, as they were formerly—and the legs are pressed into position. The cement being dry, the sewing machine is run round the edges and elsewhere, securing all together. At this stage the eyelets may be put in: a machine does this by punching the holes, pressing the eyelets into position and clenching them at high speed.

The next parts to be added are the golosh (a piece of leather or other material sewn round the lower part of the uppers) and the toe-cap. If there is any ornamental stitching or punching on the cap, this is done before it is closed on to the golosh; stitching machines adapted for doing the punching simultaneously with the lines of stitch being employed.

This part of the upper is also joined to the lining with some adhesive before stitching, the backs of the golosh are joined together by the back-strap and rows of stitching secure the golosh to the leg. When the tongue and the fabric loop at the top of the back strap have been sewn in, we have a completed upper ready for "bottoming".

In Fig. 2 the process of putting together, or closing, the pieces for an Oxford shoe are illustrated, as well as the final shape of the upper.

Putting on the sole is an art in itself, requiring a certain amount of force as well as skill; it is called "bottoming" by the trade. The appropriate last is selected and on to it is tacked the insole; this is a somewhat thinner sole than the outer one. The insole is "channelled" by means of two deep cuts (see Fig. 5: inset drawing No. 11) and the lips are turned up to make a projecting ridge that will take a stitched seam. Then the upper is put on to the last, and its edges pulled over the insole and tacked down in the manner shown by the sketch. This is called drafting.

The next process is to pleat the excess material neatly over the edge of the insole and tack it down so that its edges stand up alongside the upstanding channelled lip. In the hand-made shoe, this job requires skill, but where mass-production is the rule it is, of course performed by machinery, which is itself necessarily of a most complex nature.

SEWING THE WELT

We are now in the stage where the forceful moulding of the machine has brought the smooth surface of the upper into a perfectly good shape without a vestige of a crease. The pleated portions will be smoothed down in a machine called a pounder or knocker-up.

Next comes the welt, a strip of leather that is sewn on to the upstanding portion of the upper and the channel lips, omitting the portion that will be occupied by the heel. Several methods are employed for this and for the subsequent process of securing the welt to the outer sole; Fig. 7 illustrates some of them sectionally. But before this can

STAMPING OUT THE SOLE

Fig. 9. *Although soles are still stamped out largely by hand, various types of simple machine are used to aid the craftsman, who guides the leather as shown above.*

be done the welt has to be beaten out flat and the upstanding sewn part knocked down and levelled.

There will be a hollow space along the sole that must be filled up; for this a variety of materials may be used. Compressed cork bone or turned felt is good; cardboard has been used, though not by conscientious manufacturers! When this has been done, the outer sole, which has been cut out of the stoutest material available by means of a press machine and a press knife (shown in Fig. 4), can be attached.

One way of doing this is to sew it down by the welt, but differing types of footwear call for different treatment. Before this final securing, however, the sole has to be "laid", that is, shaped

to the contour of the last. As it is stiff and flat it would not be possible to drag it into shape by the sewing process; it must be moulded by forcible rolling.

When this forming process has been completed, the sole is stuck down with cement under pressure, after which the sewing can be done. As already mentioned, there are other methods, most notably that of riveting with short stubby nails passing through both soles, their ends being hammered down flat. Alternatively, brass wire is screwed through and cut off flush. Yet another system, employed where heavy, weather-resisting soles must be provided, is to drive wooden pegs through both. Such a method provides a boot with a stout rigid sole of great durability.

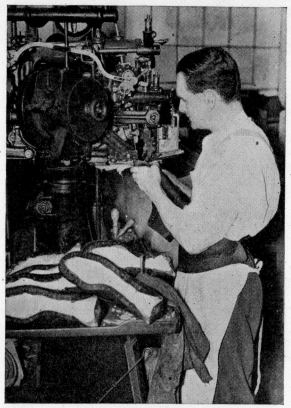

A COMPLEX SEWING MACHINE

Fig. 10. *A large variety of machines are used for the sewing operations involved in bootmaking. The operative above is tacking the uppers ready for joining to the insole.*

alternate layers, called "rands", may be of horse-shoe shape so that when the heel is compressed the part that is to bed on to the insole of the shoe will be somewhat concave in shape. In some types of fancy shoe for women, extra high heels may be made of wood, covered with thin leather to match or contrast with that of the upper.

The boot—or shoe—is now virtually complete, but has still to go through a number of finishing processes, designed to give it a good appearance. There are at least twenty of these, all carried out mechanically, beginning with the replacing of the last on which it was made by another to keep it in shape during finishing. The remaining processes include the cleaning up and trimming of any rough edges left during manufacture; the separating and tidying up of the sewing stitches of the welt and the addition to

The *veldtschoen* process (illustrated in Fig. 6) is an attempt to secure the maximum possible resistance to the seeping of water through the welt. It is an elaborate scheme calling for a double upper, but it does its work.

There remains now the provision of a heel. For most shoes this consists of a number of layers of leather cut to shape, nailed together and finally riveted on to the insole. To ensure flexibility the outer sole, as can be seen from the drawings, does not run right through over the heel portion, at all events in normal weight footwear. The heel layers, or "lifts", are not all flat;

the latter of an ornamental effect; the staining and inking of those parts left raw and their subsequent waxing and polishing. Compressing the outer edge of the sole and burnishing it does more than improve the appearance of the goods; it increases their durability and resistance to water.

Shoemaking is, as far as footwear for the masses is concerned, a highly mechanised industry, but it still calls for highly skilled operators for most of the machinery employed. We are a very long way from the stage when leather and nails will be fed into a machine—and finished shoes come out of it!

MATCHES

Early Lighting Devices. Prometheans. Friction Matches. Phosphorus and its Properties. Matchsticks from Logs. Round and Square Matches. Impregnating the Sticks. Making the Boxes. Drying and Packing.

CIVILISED life depends on an infinite number of unconsidered trifles; and among all those that help to make life easy, the humble match takes a high place. For we have long forgotten all we knew about making fire by mechanical means and without matches, or as a substitute for them, petrol lighters, we should be more helpless than a savage.

FLINT AND STEEL

Yet it is not so very long—little more than a hundred years—since getting a light was a solemn business and, by modern standards, a lengthy one. You had a contrivance—flint and steel—for striking a spark from a piece of hard stone, in principle the same as the modern petrol lighter; you had also a tinder box into which the spark fell, setting up a smelly smouldering of charred linen tinder. If you were well-to-do your tinder box contained a substance called amadou, made of a fungus treated with saltpetre, which was considered very superior to the charred linen. Then, by vigorously blowing it, you fanned the lighted tinder to a flame. You might save your breath by carrying a box of spunks—wooden splints tipped with sulphur—which ignited with a fumey spluttering when applied to the glowing tinder. No airy flick of your lighter in those not-so-far-distant days, but several minutes of anxious application, even when you were lucky enough to have dry tinder in your box.

In the early years of the nineteenth century all sorts of new-fangled notions and devices came into use, among them chemical appliances for doing away with the time-honoured flint and steel and tinder box. Thus, in the eighteen-twenties, you might have been among the bold spirits who carried an "instantaneous light box" containing a bottle of very strong sulphuric acid, into which you dipped a splint tipped with chlorate of potash. If the acid was strong enough, the splint ignited, but as it very soon became weak by absorbing moisture from the air (though not too weak to destroy your clothes and skin) it was hardly worth carrying.

Even more alarming was the once popular Promethean match, a paper spill in which was cunningly concealed a tiny glass tube of sulphuric acid

CHOPPING MATCHSTICKS

Fig. 1. *Chopping machine which cuts thin veneers into splints for matchsticks.*

165

surrounded by a chlorate of potash composition. Two pairs of pliers were needed to get a light from the Promethean match; one to hold the spill—at arm's length, one would suppose—and the other to release the acid by breaking the glass tube. Brave men were our great-grandfathers, who lit their pipes and cigars with such perilous contrivances, sometimes even dispensing with the pliers and cracking the Promethean matches in their teeth.

FRICTION MATCHES

A revolution began in 1827, when matches of the friction type, used ever since, were first sold by Mr. John Walker of Stockton-on-Tees—half-a-crown a box with a piece of coarse sandpaper thrown in. Walker's "friction matches", which were wooden splints tipped with a composition containing chlorate of potash and antimony sulphide, refused, however, to work except for the expert. Indeed, getting a light required not only a lot of friction but a great deal of dexterity, and the same was true of the Lucifer matches which appeared soon afterwards. To obtain a light from a Lucifer one had to follow these directions: "Place the folded part of the Sand Paper next to the hand, the black end of the Match between; press moderately with the finger and thumb; then withdraw it briskly and the effect of the friction will produce instant light. N.B.—If possible, avoid inhaling the gas that escapes from the combustion of the Black Composition. Persons whose lungs are delicate should by no means use the Lucifers". Equally dangerous were the phosphorus matches which followed, for they often ignited without the formality of striking! Bryant and May made the first British safety matches in 1861. The idea was—and still is—that a very small quantity of phosphorus on the outside of the match box ignites a less combustible chemical on the match head. The friction caused by striking the match generates enough heat to make the phosphorus burn.

Phosphorus is a very curious element. It has to be kept in water, for it burns in air at ordinary temperatures. It glows in the dark, and the greenish light is burning phosphorus vapour.

Match making used to be very unhealthy, owing to the very poisonous nature of phosphorus. The workers suffered from the horrible disease once known as "phossy jaw" in which first the teeth and then the jaw itself died and rotted away; but a discovery made in 1898 by two French chemists put an end to these dangers. They found that phosphorus is an allotropic element; in other words, that it can be made to arrange its atoms into molecules in different ways. This remarkable property of allotrophy, or "variety of form", is best exemplified by the element carbon, which presents us with such very dissimilar forms as diamonds and charcoal. Phosphorus can arrange itself either in an intensely poisonous white (or yellow) form, or in the entirely harmless red form, and in 1906 an international convention at Berne made the use of yellow phosphorus in matches illegal in all civilised countries.

MATCH FORESTS

We strike a lot of matches—so many indeed that the number is quite fantastic. Tens of thousands of trees, spruce and aspen poplar, straight and free from knots (from growing closely together in the dense northern forests) go to the sawmills at the match factories. Circular saws reduce them to logs 2 or 3 feet long; the bark is then stripped and the logs travel on a conveyor to the machine that transforms them by stages into splints and matchsticks (Fig. 2).

VENEER ⅒ INCH THICK →

SPLINT CUTTING GUILLOTINE

BLOCK OF 150 SHEETS READY FOR GUILLOTINE – 9 INS. WIDE

750 SPLINTS AT EACH STRIKE

IMPREGNATING DRUM

DRUM REVOLVES ON BEARINGS

IMPREGNATING SOLUTION

SPLINTS BLOWN ALONG PIPE ON TO SHARING SCREEN

SHAKING BELT TO MATCH MAKING MACHINE

WASTE AND UNDERSIZE SPLINTS DROP OUT

SPLINTS SHAKE DOWN TIDILY

FROM LOG TO MATCHSTICK

Fig. 2. *Diagrammatic view showing method of reducing log to splints. Thin sheets are peeled from a circular log, stacked into piles and sheared by a guillotine. The splints are then impregnated, dried and screened, and are ready to be made into matches.*

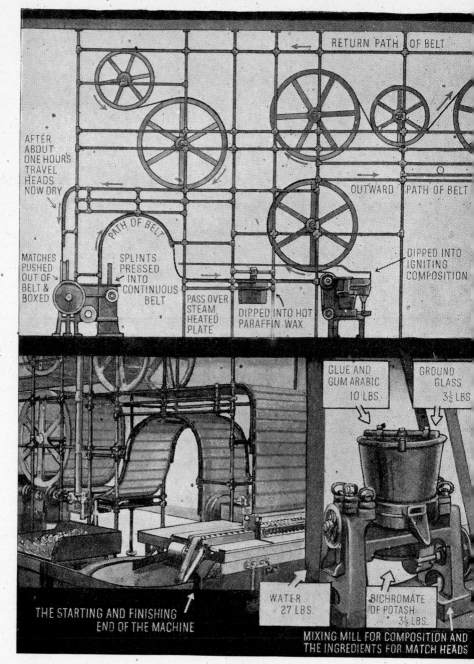

RETURN PATH OF BELT

AFTER
ABOUT
ONE HOUR'S
TRAVEL
HEADS
NOW DRY

OUTWARD PATH OF BELT

PATH OF BELT

MATCHES
PUSHED
OUT OF
BELT &
BOXED

SPLINTS
PRESSED
INTO
CONTINUOUS
BELT

PASS OVER
STEAM
HEATED
PLATE

DIPPED INTO HOT
PARAFFIN WAX

DIPPED INTO
IGNITING
COMPOSITION

GLUE AND
GUM ARABIC
10 LBS.

GROUND
GLASS
3½ LBS.

WATER
27 LBS.

BICHROMATE
OF POTASH
3½ LBS.

THE STARTING AND FINISHING
END OF THE MACHINE

MIXING MILL FOR COMPOSITION AND
THE INGREDIENTS FOR MATCH HEADS

HEADS ARE PUT ON AS THE SPLINTS

Fig. 3. *About 720,000 matches will be in this machine at one time, following a lengthy course which takes almost an hour. At the end of their journey they are pushed out and loaded*

SULPHUR
1½ LBS.

CHLORATE
OF POTASH
33½ LBS.

MANGANESE
DIOXIDE
3½ LBS.

OXIDE
OF IRON
7½ LBS.

DRYING PROGRESS

COMPOSITION WELLS

ROTATING BRUSHES

DRYING BOX

BOXES FOR PAINTING

PAINTING THE IGNITION PATCH
ON THE FILLED BOXES

TRAVEL ROUND AN ENDLESS BELT

into the waiting boxes. Thereafter the boxes go to another machine to have the ignition patches painted on their sides. From start to finish, the whole process is automatic.

E.T.T.S.—F*

Round matches are cut out of blocks, a match-length in thickness, by hollow steel dies which descend vertically. As the die descends a perforated plate, one of a continuous band of such plates, comes into position beneath the board and the splints are pushed into the perforations, in which they are firmly held and ready to be carried on the continuous band through the processes that turn them into matches.

SQUARE MATCHES

To make square matches it is first necessary to cut the logs into sheets of the thickness of a single match—usually one-tenth of an inch. Thin sheets or veneers of wood are wanted in furniture making, in box-making and in enormous quantities for plywood. So the match-maker uses veneer cutters for bringing his logs to a suitable size for matchsticks. The veneer cutter makes the log unwind itself, as it were, into a long, thin flexible sheet. The log is firmly held between clutches in a sort of lathe and revolved against a stationary knife; the knife then cuts the log, taking off a shaving of the required thickness (Fig. 1). A feed mechanism keeps the diminishing log always pressed against the knife, which consequently continues to cut the veneer until there is no more log left to cut. The veneers are pushed into another machine, arranged in neat stacks of sheets exactly alike in length, width and thickness, to be guillotined, first lengthwise and then crosswise. In no time the veneer becomes an avalanche of matchsticks—56,000 tumbling out of the machine in one minute.

Safety matches must be impregnated. If you cut an ordinary splint of wood the thickness of a match and light it you will find that the flame travels down the splint leaving a red-hot ember that continues to glow for some time before it curls and falls, still glowing. A good match leaves no ember; the burnt part should be quite harmless immediately the flame goes out.

The newly-cut matchsticks are put in large perforated drums and immersed, drums and all, in a tank of chemical solution—boric acid is sometimes used. After a good soak in the solution the drums are hoisted from the tank and an overhead traverser takes charge of them. They are then connected to gearing that sets them revolving, so that centrifugal force can fling the moisture out.

It takes some hours to get them dry. In the meantime (since a safety-match is useless without its box) we may observe the box-making department at work (Fig. 4). There are three pieces in a matchbox; one for the outer, or cover, and two for the inner, or box proper—a bottom and sides.

These parts must be cut and assembled, then joined to form inner and outer respectively by pasting paper round them. The veneer-cutters prepare the material, cutting from a log a shaving only about $\frac{1}{30}$th of an inch thick. As the shaving comes off, scoring knives mark it in the exact place where it will presently be folded. It is then sliced into widths. One set of widths is conveyed to the machines that make the outers; the other set goes to the machines that make the inners.

BOX-MAKING MACHINES

Each machine is an extremely complicated substitute for the dexterity of human hands, but the swiftly moving cams and cranks by which it operates are less liable to error than are our fingers, and are far more expeditious. As the scored widths are fed to the machine that makes the outer, they become folded round a steel former the exact size of the inner. While thus folded and held, the printed label comes to the same spot, is cut off at the right

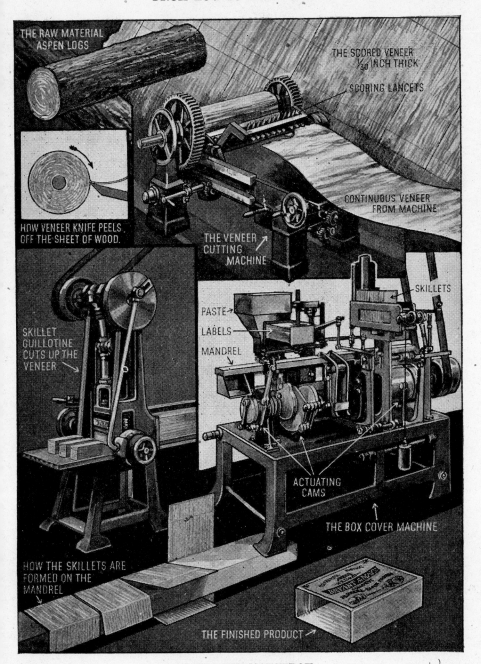

THE RAW MATERIAL
ASPEN LOGS

THE SCORED VENEER
1/30 INCH THICK

SCORING LANCETS

HOW VENEER KNIFE PEELS
OFF THE SHEET OF WOOD.

CONTINUOUS VENEER
FROM MACHINE

THE VENEER
CUTTING
MACHINE

SKILLETS

PASTE

LABELS

MANDREL

SKILLET
GUILLOTINE
CUTS UP THE
VENEER

ACTUATING
CAMS

THE BOX COVER MACHINE

HOW THE SKILLETS ARE
FORMED ON THE
MANDREL

THE FINISHED PRODUCT

MAKING THE MATCHBOX

Fig. 4. *By machines of the type illustrated, matchboxes are produced in vast numbers, from a thin veneer which is peeled continuously by a knife edge from aspen logs.*

moment and pasted round the folded outer. Surplus paste is wiped off, the steel former is withdrawn and the outer gently ejected on to a conveyor that takes it, one of an endless procession, to a drying chamber (Fig. 5). It is a matter of unerring co-ordination; the result, one outer per second per machine.

FINISHING BOXES

Meanwhile, in another machine, the side of the inner is folded round another steel former. The bottom is fed up to it, paper from a reel is pasted, cut, folded over the bottom and up the sides and neatly turned in over the edges. So the inner likewise falls on to a conveyor, one per second per machine, and is carried off to be dried. The conveyors not only carry damp inners and outers to the drying chambers; they also bring them down unceasingly, when dried, to a third machine. Inners and outers enter this machine by separate slots; they are then made to face each other and the inner is pushed into the outer.

We may now return to the impregnated splints that will presently fill our empty boxes. They are in the impregnating drums but are not all perfect; some are crooked, others are broken, and these must be sorted out. A blast of air carries them, good and bad, up shoots on to sloping screens which are vibrating. The imperfect splints are shaken through the holes in the screen, while the others arrive safely at the bottom and fall on to a vibrating belt moving at right angles to the screen. This belt is divided into slot-like compartments into which the sticks are jolted, and hundreds of thousands of matchsticks, all lying side by side, are ready for the continuous match machine.

The essence of the machine (Fig. 3) is a continuous band that travels back and forth along different planes, up and down, over and under, always at a new level. This band is composed of steel plates closely perforated with little holes—hundreds of thousands of holes in all. In every hole a splint is firmly held, to become a perfect match, ready for its box, after an hour's ride through the machine—look at the end of a match, and you can see that it is slightly misshapen as a result of that journey.

An amazing mechanism brings the matches into position so that no match escapes its hole in the moving band. The conveyor, as we know, has brought the splints from the screens; they now pass into a duct and are carried into the machine where, once more under the influence of a joggling mechanism, a plunger presses them into the holes as the band moves slowly past. The first thing that happens to the closely-set procession as it travels through the machine is immersion in a bath of molten paraffin wax. Automatic feed keeps the wax always at exactly the same level, however many thousands or millions of matches absorb it.

WAXING

In the continuous match machine there is a chain of self-acting buckets of wax, and as each bucket reaches the bath it engages a trigger which causes it to tip over, thus discharging its contents. That goes on all the time or, as occasionally happens, until a match falls out of its hole in the travelling belt and puts the bucket-tripping gear out of action. The result of such a mishap would be that the belt continued to carry matches through a bath which was deficient in wax. So the bath is provided with an electric contact which switches on a warning light immediately the wax falls below the correct level.

From the wax bath the belt carries the matches into another bath containing the igniting composition. At this immersion, the splints become matches as we know them, but by no means ready for striking, as the wet heads have yet to be dried. So the belt carries them up tier after tier of the lofty machine while currents of air blow upon them. At the end of an hour they are not only dry and ready for their boxes, but have arrived almost at the point from which they started. At this point, where they were pushed into the belt, they are now punched out of it and fall into compartments, the size of matchboxes, on a belt travelling at right angles. Coming up to meet them is an endless train of empty boxes; a self-acting plunger pushes the inner half of the box out of the cover and in go the matches. A good shake settles them down clear of the cover, which is instantly pushed over the inner by the plunger. Almost a million matches, fifty to a box, come off this machine every hour. It remains only to put the boxes up in dozens and the dozens into grosses. So the stream of full boxes flows to the packing machine whose shuttle-like movements of slides, rockers and levers uncannily suggest the movements of human hands.

It whisks a sheet of paper into place; twelve boxes of matches come into position; arms fold the paper over; the package is pushed forwards and more arms neatly turn the ends in. The wrapped package then goes forward to another machine which flicks a second piece of paper into place—this time the printed label. Once more, arms, rockers and slides perform their task, producing packs of a dozen boxes of matches at the rate of one pack in each second.

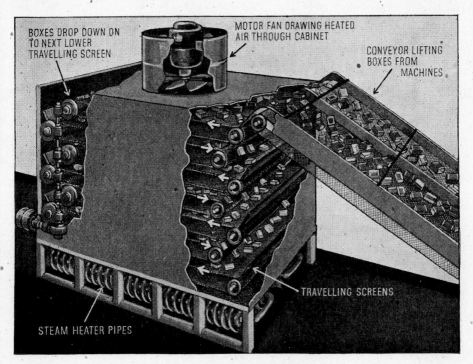

DRYING THE MATCHBOXES

Fig. 5. *Drying cabinet with outer cover broken away to show travelling wire screens which carry boxes through the hot air current drawn up from steam pipes below.*

CASTING WIRE BARS

A preliminary stage in the manufacture of pins and needles. Molten brass flows from the spout of the furnace into moulds fitted to a turntable, which is turned by the attendants as each mould is filled. These moulds form the metal into bars which will at a later stage of production be rolled into heavy gauge, then drawn into finer gauge wire.

174

NEEDLES AND PINS

Various Uses of Pins and Needles. Types for all Purposes. How They Developed.
Modern Materials. Wire-drawing and Cutting. Pointing and Polishing.
Dangers in Old Time Processes. Sealing and Stamping. Electro-Plating,
Whitening and Japanning. Packing and Selling.

IN these days many of us do not realise how much present-day civilisation owes to the advent of the humble needle. Though it seems to be a very commonplace article, it is one that is of the greatest importance, for without it civilisation could hardly exist. Think, for instance, of the thousand-and-one uses to which a needle is put—our clothes, our boots, many of our household goods, even the books we read, all are made with its aid.

Needles were necessary even in prehistoric times; both bone and metal needles have been found in Egyptian tombs and in ancient cave dwellings. These needles, which were made of fish-bone, wood, or ivory, were thick and heavy as compared with modern needles. Although some had eyes at the end or in the middle, many had only a hook at the end, like the modern crochet hook. Until comparatively recent times the Red Indians and other primitive tribes used the slender wing-bones of birds as needles, drawing sinews through the hides to sew them into garments.

THE FIRST METAL NEEDLES

The manufacture of needles, which were probably brought to Europe by the Moors, began in England about the middle of the 17th century. At first needles were made by hand—a laborious process—but later wonderful machines manufactured them with absolute accuracy by the million, whereas in times past hand workers had turned them out by the mere dozen at a time.

In those days, of course, the making of needles was dependent on the skill of each individual workman, with the result that some needles were better made than others; today they are made entirely by these ingenious machines which are so accurate that every needle they produce is of a standard uniform quality and pattern. Today, the centre of the British industry is at Redditch, where the making of needles for every purpose is a staple industry. Thousands of workpeople are employed, and a tour round the many factories would convince the most sceptical of the undoubted importance of the needle-making trade.

SPECIAL TYPES

There are many types of needle besides the sewing needle. Special needles are required for leather work and sailcloth, for instance; there are the familiar knitting needles, crochet needles, harness, mattress, upholsterers' and machine needles, as well as several other kinds. Special varieties such as surgical needles—which are curiously twisted and often of a semicircular shape—are made by particular processes. The manufacture here described will be confined to sewing needles as representative of the processes involved (Fig. 4).

Needles today are made from very high quality steel wire, perfectly round and straight and free from all surface blemishes. The wire must be of such a quality that it does not break when struck by the various tools under which it has to pass in the course of manufacture.

Moreover, the quality must be such that when hardened and tempered the wire forms a good springy needle which although it will bend to a considerable degree without breaking, will at once spring straight again.

In the first place, the wire is drawn to the exact thickness of the needle required and, in its original form, may vary from a hair's breadth to nearly 1 in. in diameter (Figs. 1 and 3). It must not be thicker or thinner by even half a thousandth of an inch than the finished product is to be. This wire, which comes from the wire-drawing factory in the form of a coil of several hundred yards, is put on to a machine that automatically cuts it up to the required lengths and at the same time makes each little length perfectly straight. These lengths of wire are exactly the length of two needles, because needles are made end to end and cut later.

After the wire has been thus cut the lengths are grouped together in bundles weighing about 14 lb. to 28 lb. each and heated in a furnace until almost red hot. This is done to "kill" any acids that may have been used in the wire-drawing processes because, if allowed to remain on the surface, they would cause pit marks in the steel known as "flecks", which would be very difficult to remove.

STRAIGHTENING WIRE

Whilst the bundle of wire is hot, the wires go through a process that rubs them together. This rubbing of one wire against another has the effect of straightening them even more perfectly than was possible in the straightening machine. The wires are now put through a machine that automatically points them at one end. After all the wires have passed through the machine, they are reversed and put through again so as to point them at the other end. It takes from fifteen to thirty minutes to point

about 30,000 wires. The pointing is done by passing the wires one after another across the top of a large carborundum stone, 24 in. in diameter, that is rotating at a very high speed.

In the days before the Factory Acts came into being in England, the pointing dust floated about the workshop, causing severe chest trouble to the workmen. To protect themselves, workers used to tie a handkerchief over the nose and mouth to prevent themselves from inhaling the dust, but this was not effective, and they usually died young.

EXHAUST FANS

Because of this danger the rates of pay in the industry were very high, and needle manufacturers gave their men a quart of milk daily. Today the pointing dust is extracted by exhaust fans and carried away to a pit where it is allowed to settle; it is eventually sold to firework manufacturers as an ingredient for making the familiar "sparklers".

The next process is to put the wires through an automatic machine in which an emery band passes across their centres and removes any scale that may be on them. This is done because in the next process—stamping—the dies would be clogged if there were any scale remaining on the wires. In the stamping process the wires are placed beneath a pair of dies that impress the two eyes of the needles in the middle of the wire. This is only an impression and not a piercing; the metal therefore remains in the actual eyes with a small flattened head, called a "splash", left by the stamping dies around where the two eyes will be. In the case of large needles —and some needles are as thick as $\frac{1}{4}$ in. —the stamping is done under a power press, a drop hammer or a kick stamp. In these presses one wire is put in at a time, but in the case of thinner needles the wires pass automatically underneath

BRASS WIRE BEING DRAWN INTO FINER GAUGE

Fig. 1. *After the brass castings have been rolled sufficiently in the foundry to reduce them to heavy gauge wire, the wire is drawn into a finer gauge on wire-drawing blocks. Pins are now made of brass, mild steel and carbon steel wire, and are finished by various processes, such as electro-plating, whitening and black-japanning, according to the purpose for which they are intended and the quality of finish required.*

the dies and are impressed at the rate of about 200 per minute.

The next process is to remove the thin pieces of metal from the eyes, and this is done by passing the wires through a machine fitted with two very fine punches that exactly fit each eye. These punches must give a perfectly clean cut, for if they did not a tiny fragment of jagged metal would be left which would cut the thread when the needle was used. Here again, the thicker needles are eyed under power presses or hand-fly presses, the thinner needles under high-speed automatic machines.

The "splash" left from the stamping process now has to be removed. The wires, with the impression of two eyes in them, are strung together by threading strips of metal through the eyes, one through each, on the double row of wires. The strips are known as "spits"

and the operation of threading them as "spitting". As a result of this process all the splashes on the wires are now standing parallel together. The wires are held in a clamp about 5 in. in width, the splash being held against a grindstone rotating at a high speed, which results in all the splash on one side of the wires being ground away. When this has been done, the clamp is turned over and the splash on the other side is removed.

Next, the wires have to be broken in two without the spits being removed, so that after this process the needles are single. Although the splash has been ground away on the sides, or cheeks, of the needles, the head still has some little splash on each side of it, and this must be removed. Consequently, the wires are again picked up in the clamp and the head pressed lightly against the grindstone to remove the splash. The

INTERIOR OF A PIN FACTORY

Fig. 2. *General view of the plant. This plant produces enormous quantities of brass, mild steel and carbon steel pins at the rate of six or seven million a day.*

REDUCING THE GAUGE OF STEEL WIRE

Fig. 3. *In this picture steel wire is seen entering the draw-bench measuring 96 thousandths of an inch in thickness, and being reduced to a thickness of 29 thousandths.*

process is repeated by turning over the clamp so that the splash on the other side of the head may be removed. Finally, the spits are taken out of the eyes. We have now a needle perfectly shaped; as, however, it is made of soft wire it is still in the soft state and easily bent. To overcome this defect it must be hardened, which is the object of the next process.

The needles are spread out on a pan and placed in a very hot furnace, where they are heated to a bright red. The actual temperature to which they are raised is most important and is controlled by means of pyrometers. Experience also plays a large part, for a hardener knows exactly what temperature is required for any particular quality or type of needle. When all the needles in the furnace have reached the desired temperature, they are immersed at once

in a vat of cold oil in the case of the best quality needles, or water for the cheaper qualities. The sudden change in the temperature has the effect of hardening the steel, but makes the needles so brittle that they will break like matchsticks under the slightest pressure.

Needles that break are of no use, of course, so in order to give them the required degree of springiness they are heated again in a rather cooler furnace until they reach the correct temperature, when they are allowed to cool slowly until quite cold. This tempering process imparts to them the necessary resistance.

Next, the needles must be polished. Some 50,000 or 60,000 needles are wrapped in sack-cloth—in the form of "roly-poly" puddings—tied up with strong string. Before each bundle is tied up the workman sees that all the

PICTORIAL DIAGRAM SHOWING SUCCESSIVE

Fig. 4. *Cut to the length of two needles, the steel wires are annealed in the furnace (1), straightened (2), pointed both ends (3), and stamped and punched (4). When the burr has been removed (5), the threaded wires are broken in half (6), and the burr from the breakage*

RUBBING AND STRAIGHTENING WIRE "BLANKS" ②

CURBED BAR

③ POINTING BOTH ENDS

AUTOMATIC FEED

CONCAVE GRINDING WHEEL

DUST EXTRACTOR

REMOVING BURR FROM EYES ⑤

FEED HOPPER

STAMPING & EYEING ④

EYEING PUNCH

SPIRAL FEED

GRINDER

NEEDLES LACED TOGETHER

ES BROKEN) TWO NEEDLES ⑥

STAMPING DIE

SETTING POINTS ⑭

GRINDER

BUFF WHEEL ⑮

FINAL POLISHING

FINISHED NEEDLES 'STUCK' IN PACKETS

⑯ FINISHED NEEDLE (Much Enlarged)

STAGES IN THE MANUFACTURE OF NEEDLES

removed. Hardened by being heated and quenched suddenly (8, 9, 10) they are then reheated to prevent brittleness. Blueing the eyes (11), scouring (12), sorting (13) and grinding and polishing (14 and 15) are the final stages before they are packed into neat containers.

ONE TYPE OF PIN-MAKING MACHINE

Fig. 5. *This machine is fed from a coil of wire which comes out the other side in the form of pins.*

bundle and the process is repeated for three or four days, until a fuller polish has been obtained. Of course, the abrasive is used up and the string and sacking wear away, so that fresh lots have to be used every time. This method, which is called "scouring", arose in the old days when needles were hand-made. A workman would be sitting at his bench, hammering or drilling the eye into a piece of wire, so as to make a few needles. He found that those he had previously made could be polished by rubbing them with his foot on the floor as he sat at work. The present method is identical in procedure although carried out on a larger scale.

After the needles have been inspected and the defective ones thrown away, they pass out of the scouring mill. They are now all "higgledy-piggledy", any number from 50,000 to 100,000 of them being in a tangled mass. The first thing to do is to get them into some kind of order, so that they can be readily handled. To do this a woman places two or three handfuls of them into a tray about a foot square, with vertical sides. Holding the tray fairly level, she shakes them to and fro, at the same time pulling the blade of a knife through the needles. Gradually the tangled mass shakes itself into one in which the needles all lie parallel to each other. After a final shake they can be removed on the blade of the knife and placed on a table for handling easily. Here they are stacked up, then wrapped into small parcels each containing 2,000 needles, and the parcels are put into stock until required.

needles are lying parallel with each other along the length of the bundle; he then puts among them emery powders, abrasive materials and soft soap. The bundle, which is about 20 in. in length and from 4 to 6 in. in diameter, is now placed in a long trough. On top of the trough is a runner or long board that slides to and fro, so that the bundle beneath it will revolve in an opposite direction as the board above it moves backwards and forwards. It is left in the "to-and-fro" state for about twelve hours, when it is removed and opened up.

When the needles have been washed in hot water and soap-suds they are found to be slightly polished. They are, therefore, wrapped up again in another

Subsequently, they are packed up into little papers containing 25 needles or so. Alternatively, they may be put into pieces of black paper, or, in better class packets, stuck through special black needle cloth and finally placed into a small envelope with a window.

Some needles are electro-plated and many have the eyes gilded. The electro-plating preserves the finish and makes them less liable to rust in hot climates; the gilded eyes not only decorate them but make threading easier.

The use of pins, like that of needles, dates from prehistoric times when thorns served the purpose. During the Second World War, owing to the dearth of pins in France, natives of the French colonies in North Africa collected cactus spikes and sold them to the French as substitutes for pins.

A couple of centuries ago the making of pins was a lengthy and expensive business. Eight or ten men were employed to carry out the various processes—cutting the wire to its proper length, pointing it on a grindstone, making the head, polishing etc. The making of the head was the most difficult part of the work. This used to be done by placing a tiny disk or washer of metal on the blunt end of the wire and riveting it on, or twisting a small portion of the wire and hammering into a head. This process made the manufacture of pins in those days a costly affair, and it was this which gave rise to the expression "pin money", applied to an allowance made by a husband to his wife, for dress; pins, in the days before cheap buttons and zip fasteners were known, being a very important item.

It was this making of the head that also puzzled those who tried to invent a machine for manufacturing pins. In England this difficulty was solved by Lemuel Wright, who made the first machine in 1824.

The present-day pin-making machine is almost entirely automatic, performing all stages of manufacture until the whitening and polishing process is reached. Many such machines are capable of turning out some three to four hundred pins every minute (Fig. 5). They vary slightly in the detail of their construction, for each firm has added its own little gadgets. The pin shop shown in Fig. 2 produces between 6 and 7 million pins a day.

The pin-wire used in the manufacture of the ordinary pin is made of mild steel,

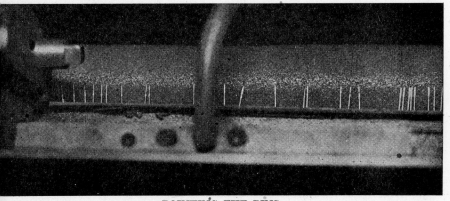

POINTING THE PINS

Fig. 6. *Illustrating the various stages of the pointing process performed by revolving mills. As the cut wires enter the machine on the right they are quite blunt.*

ELECTROPLATING PINS OF MILD STEEL

Fig. 7. *The pins are placed in baskets and immersed in a solution which, by electrolytic action, deposits a coating of tin upon them. These girls are draining off excess liquid.*

which varies in gauge according to the size of the pin desired. The finest gauge is used for those made for entomologists. Brass pins are made of hard drawn brass wire, while the best class of steel pins, used by dressmakers and others, are of high quality steel wire. The wire is brought to the factory rolled on drums or reels. This gives it a curve, so the first process performed by the machine, which is a comparatively small contrivance, is to straighten it.

The curved wire, on being introduced into the machine, is caught by rollers revolving at high speed and by lateral steel blocks, which straighten it further. A small portion of the wire projects beyond these blocks and is immediately struck by a steel punch or die which gives the pin a head; the wire is at once cut to the required length. Immediately this process is complete, the blunt pins slide into a sloping groove which is just wide enough to let the shank of the pin slip through, but too narrow to allow the head to pass.

The consequence is that the half-made pins hang down in rows held by the heads. This slot is never made of steel, as the magnetic quality of this metal would attract the pins into heaps and prevent them sliding to their required position. Metal containing bronze is, therefore, always used instead.

The blunt ends of the pins now hanging down in rows are ready to be sharpened (Fig. 6). The ends are brought into contact with a revolving roller made of carborundum, sometimes termed a cutter. After being pointed, the pins slide out of their slots into receptacles below to be scoured and cleaned. This is done in what is termed the barrelling shop. Here they are given their silvery appearance by being put into a bath of granulated tin and oxalic acid. In the case of brass pins, which, as a rule, are not saleable in their yellow condition, the silvering is done by first of all washing them in argol, a pink deposit left at the bottom of a cask of wine when it ferments; this forms bitartrate of potassium or, as it is often called, cream of tartar. After that they receive the same treatment as the ordinary pin.

Iron pins, a lower-grade article, are silvered by the electrolytic method (Fig. 7). They are put into an iron pot and covered with powdered tin, together with a small amount of oxalic acid. They are then covered with water and boiled for several hours. This gives them their silvery appearance. In order to remove any excrescences that may have clung to them and to give them a final polish, all pins are put into a revolving barrel of sawdust.

Steel pins, used by dressmakers, the stationery trade and other special businesses, and made of tempered and hardened steel wire, are hardened in what is known in the trade as a "muffle", which is a kind of oven placed in a furnace. They are then tempered by immersion in oil. This process requires skilled artificers, just as does the tempering of razors and swords.

The polishing of these pins is effected by placing them in revolving drums, containing steel shot, which continue to revolve for several days. When finished the pins are almost equal to needles in sharpness and temper.

The variety of pins is much greater than might be supposed. The ordinary pin, about an inch in length, is known in the trade as a "short white". The manufacturer sells his pins by weight: a pound is the usual standard of measure. A pound of short white numbers about four thousand, perhaps rather more. Those used by entomologists, however, are sold by the ounce, one ounce containing close upon five thousand of these extremely small pins.

PIN PACKING BY MACHINERY

The second girl from the right is shown emptying pins into a hopper. The pins then slide down grooves held by their heads and are stamped by a treadle into sheets of paper.

THE MENDER AT WORK

Fig. 1. *The intricate system of colours that appears on the design is accurately transferred by the looms. Occasionally a thread may break, causing a gap in the design, and menders inspect the carpets for these flaws and sew in the missing thread.*

CARPETS

Spinning the Yarn. Woollen and Worsted Styles. Gilling and Dyeing. Spool Axminster. Designing Department. Jacquard Wilton. Two- and Three-Shot Fabrics. Plain Carpets. Tufted Axminster. Chenille Weaving. Finishing.

MAKING a carpet is rather like fitting together the pieces of a huge jigsaw puzzle. All the parts must fit perfectly and no part must be missing, or the whole scheme falls through. Carpet manufacture, unlike the greater part of textile production, depends on other sections of the trade that are industries in themselves. All are vitally necessary for the completion of something over which the greatest of trouble is taken in making and choosing both design and material, only to be put on the floor for people to walk on!

SPINNING THE PILE YARN

The first important process in carpet manufacture is the preparation of the wool that forms the "pile", or surface, of the carpet. As in woollen manufacture in general, the raw wool from the sheep is blended and washed, then sent to the spinning mills for conversion into yarn. The actual spinning of the yarn is done either on the woollen system or on the worsted principle.

In the former the loose wool is fed into a carding machine, or "engine". A carding engine consists mainly of two parts—the scribbler and the card—with an intermediate feed between them. Cylinders and rollers covered with fine pins are driven at different speeds and in different directions, the object being to open up the matted wool and lay the fibres more or less parallel to one another. At the end of the machine the wool is removed in the form of a fine, wide web. This is split up into perhaps a hundred ends that are rubbed into round threads and wound on to several spools at once.

These spools are then put into a "mule"—a machine consisting of a fixed frame carrying rollers on which rest the carding-engine spools. A carriage with a row of upright spindles parallel to the fixed frame moves to and from the spools of threads. As it moves, it draws the threads to the required thickness and whilst running outwards gives them a twist; when coming in, it winds the spun yarn on to the spindle. In this form it is known as a "cop", being cylindrical in shape but tapered at the top and bottom. When the cops are sufficiently large they are removed and put into a twisting frame, where the threads of two or perhaps three cops are twisted together. Here the yarn threads pass between rollers and are twisted and wound on to large bobbins simultaneously. Next, the twisting bobbins containing the two-fold or three-fold yarn are emptied and the yarn made into hanks and bundled for storage. The alternative worsted spinning system requires rather more processes to produce the yarn than the woollen principle; because of this—and because longer and more lustrous wool is used—the finished product is smoother and the fibres straighter. The yarn itself has a sheen that makes it characteristic in the cloth. The preliminary processing before carding is the same as in the woollen system—namely, in the blending to obtain the required type of raw material and in the scouring. The carding process is similar to this, with the exception of a few essentials—for instance, there is no intermediate feed and, in the final delivery, the fibres are more nearly parallel to one another. They are taken off in a wide web and run into one twistless rope-like "sliver" which is wound into a ball.

The rope-like product of the carding engine is drawn successively finer in each of the six or so drawing operations. This is achieved by feeding the slivers into the machine with slow-running rollers, while a faster-running pair of rollers at the front draws the wool until it is of the finer thread required.

GILLING OPERATIONS

The first two operations are those of gilling, where the sliver is drawn finer and through rows of pins that straighten as well as open out the wool. The first gill-box turns out the wool in an untwisted sliver; the second gill-box delivers it in ball form. The succeeding operations draw the slivers finer, give them twist and wind them on to bobbins. In the last operation—that of spinning—the threads are drawn out to the required thickness. Thereafter, the thread is dealt with in a similar manner to the woollen yarn, being twisted two- or three-fold; it is generally two-folded again before being bundled for storage.

The yarn—either woollen or worsted —now goes through the dyehouse into the preparatory departments and then to the weaving sheds.

Before dyeing, the hanks of yarn are scoured, in soap and hot water, to remove oil and dirt picked up during the spinning operations. The dyeing machine is a large tank with steam coils in the bottom for boiling the dye liquor. At one end there is a propeller that causes the liquor to flow through the hanks. The latest machines are made of stainless steel and have a lid from which the hanks of yarn are hung on stainless steel rods; when, therefore, the lid is lowered on to the machine the hanks are immersed in the dye liquor. The dyer decides how much dyestuff has to be used, according to the depth of shade and the weight of yarn to be dyed, also the colours to be used to obtain the desired shade.

After the necessary time has elapsed, the hanks are withdrawn and compared with the sample that the dyer is matching. If they are not sufficiently near, more dyestuffs are added, calculated to effect the requisite alteration, and the procedure is repeated. When the shade is exact the hanks of yarn are removed, rinsed in cold water and partially dried in a hydro-extractor, which is a perforated metal cage that revolves at a high speed, the water being removed from the hanks by centrifugal force. The dyed yarn is finally dried in a steam-heated drying machine, and is now ready for the weaving processes.

There are three principal processes— those of Spool Axminster, Jacquard Wilton (Fig. 4) and Chenille weaving.

AXMINSTER DESIGN

In Spool Axminster weaving the dyed yarn is wound from the hanks on to bobbins, and these are placed into a setting frame along with any other colours necessary. The design to be woven has previously been put on to squared paper by the designing department, each square on the paper representing one tuft (Fig. 2). One row of squares is done at a time, and for each of the coloured squares, the corresponding thread of yarn is pulled through a comb at the front of the frame. When the row is completed all the ends of yarn are fastened to a long bobbin and are then wound on to it until the bobbin or spool is full of yarn.

This procedure is repeated for the remaining rows of the design, so that

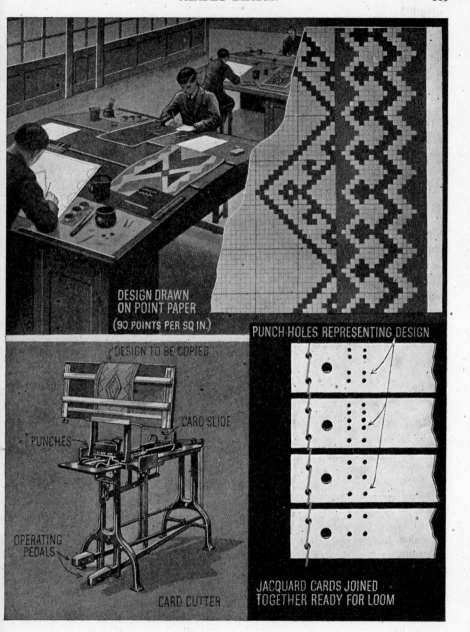

IN THE DESIGNING DEPARTMENT

Fig. 2. *The first stage in carpet making is the preparation of the design. Skilled artists and draughtsmen draw this on finely ruled paper, from which the card cutter punches the patterns. These cards are then attached to the Jacquard machine on the loom and they control the lifting of the* WARP *threads for the passage of the* WEFT *shuttle.*

each spool has coloured yarns on it representing the corresponding row of the design paper. Each of the ends is threaded through a tube held in a frame fixed to the spool, the threading being done by passing a row of hooks through the tubes and pulling the threads back with them in the order of the pattern.

ON THE LOOM

It will be seen that if tufts are taken off the spools in their correct order and placed row to row, the tufts will form the design as drawn on the design paper, and this is what the Axminster loom does (Fig. 5). Each spool in turn is taken by the loom from a moving carrier (Fig. 3), and the ends of the yarns protruding from the tubes are pushed between the warp threads coming from the beams—or large iron bobbins—at the back of the loom. The warp threads—consisting of cotton and perhaps jute—help to bind the tufts of wool and also form the back of the carpet. The weft, passed from side to side of the loom by a long needle, crosses the warp and binds the woollen yarn ends into the fabric. The row of threads is then cut free from the spool, leaving a row of coloured ends in the carpet. As each of the spools is taken in its turn, the row of tufts is beaten well up to its neighbour, and so the design and the carpet are built up. These operations are repeated until the spools are empty. The quality of the carpet will be governed by the height at which the pile tufts are cut, and by the number of rows of tufts that are put in per inch.

In Jacquard Wilton weaving the dyed yarn is also put on to small bobbins that are placed into frames at the back of the loom. There are five, or sometimes six, of these frames, each containing as many bobbins as there are ends in the width of cloth to be woven. Generally, the bobbins of each frame contain yarn of one colour, so that the Jacquard fabric has a complement of five or six colours. Sometimes "planting" is carried out—that is, the placing of a few bobbins of a different colour in a frame—and by judicious use a four-frame fabric may be made to look like a five-frame, and so on. Great care must be exercised, however, or stripes will appear in the finished pattern.

All the ends from the bobbins are drawn through the "harness", or lifting gear, and passed through a kind of comb, called the "reed". There is one thread from each frame through one space, or "split", in the reed. Each space also has two cotton threads, called "small chains", passing through it and one or two threads of cotton or jute as a "stuffer", according to the quality of the cloth required. The small chains bind the weft, which is either jute or hemp, into the back of the fabric. The stuffer threads, which come from large beams or bobbins at the back of the loom, merely lie in the back, and help to make it strong, stiff and solid.

TWO- AND THREE-SHOT FABRICS

Wilton fabrics are either "two-shot" or "three-shot". This means that there are either two or three threads of weft per repeat of the weave structure. There is always one thread of weft showing on the back, whilst the other thread, in the case of a two-shot, binds the rows of wool pile into the back. In a three-shot cloth, two threads of weft bind the tufts.

When the loom is weaving, the "going part", carrying the reed, moves backward and forward alternately, allowing the shuttle, which carries the weft, to pass from one side of the loom to the other. As the reed moves backward, the shuttle passes across, leaving behind a thread of weft. Then the reed moves forward and "beats-up" the weft close to the woven part of the carpet.

FEEDING THE LOOM

Fig. 3. *As many as 12,000 bobbins can go to the weaving of a carpet. The operative above is watching the rows of bobbins to ensure an unbroken flow of thread.*

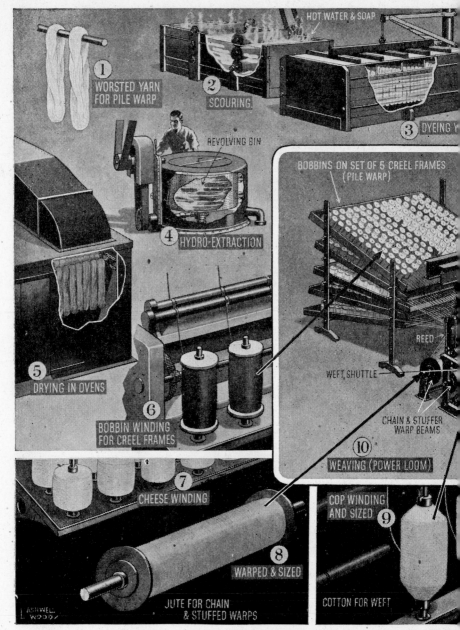

WEAVING BEAUTIFUL DESIGNS BY MACHINERY:

Fig. 4. *After the yarn (1) for the pile warp has been spun, the hanks are scoured (2) in soap and hot water to remove dirt and oil. The yarn is then dyed in a tank of boiling dye (3) and dried first in a hydro-extractor (4) and then in an oven heated by steam (5). It is then wound from the hanks on to bobbins (6) which are prepared for the loom by sizing (8).*

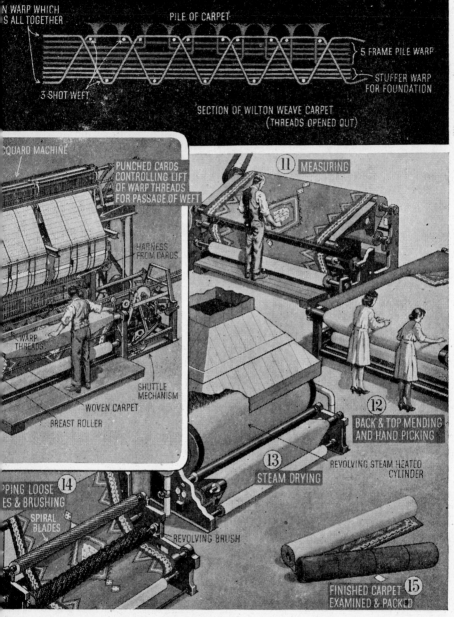

N WARP WHICH
S ALL TOGETHER

PILE OF CARPET

5 FRAME PILE WARP

STUFFER WARP
FOR FOUNDATION

3 SHOT WEFT

SECTION OF WILTON WEAVE CARPET
(THREADS OPENED OUT)

CQUARD MACHINE

PUNCHED CARDS
CONTROLLING LIFT
OF WARP THREADS
FOR PASSAGE OF WEFT

HARNESS
FROM CARDS

(11) MEASURING

WARP
THREADS

SHUTTLE
MECHANISM

WOVEN CARPET

BREAST ROLLER

(12)
BACK & TOP MENDING
AND HAND PICKING

REVOLVING STEAM HEATED
CYLINDER

(13)
STEAM DRYING

PING LOOSE (14)
ES & BRUSHING

SPIRAL
BLADES

REVOLVING BRUSH

FINISHED CARPET (15)
EXAMINED & PACKED

MAKING A WILTON PILE CARPET

The weaving process (10) is explained in the text. The processes that follow include measuring the woven carpet (11), mending any broken ends or faults that have been left in the weaving process (12), steaming in order to "burst" the yarn and increase the evenness of the effect (13), and cutting off loose "whiskers" and fibres in the cutting cylinder (14).

E.T.T.S.—G

At every second or third journey of the shuttle, the Jacquard raises the coloured woollen or worsted yarns that are required for the correct reproduction of the design. Under these threads the loom places a thin strip of steel called a wire, standing on its edge. At one end of the wire is a small, sharp blade, pointing upwards. The woollen yarns are now allowed to drop and are fastened into the back of the carpet by the weft. Thus, it may be seen that the yarn is now looped over the wire, and that when the latter is withdrawn, the blade cuts through the loops and produces the plush effect. Only one of the ends of wool in each "split" is raised at a time, the remaining four colours lying dormant in the back until their turn comes.

THE PILE

The height of the pile may be altered by using wires of different depth, some being as high as 5 in. and others barely 1 inch. Sometimes round wires are used with no blades fixed, leaving the surface uncut and in loops. This type of fabric is known as Brussels.

Plain colour carpets are woven on plain looms having no Jacquard. One large beam at the back of the loom has all the yarn on it sufficient to make the required length of carpet. Uni-coloured and mottled carpets and stair-carpets may be made on a tappet loom. Mottles are obtained by using for the pile yarn that is composed of two colours or different shades of one colour, twisted together. Stair-carpets may be made by putting threads of another colour at the sides of the beam holding the yarn threads, thus causing band borders to appear at the sides of the woven carpet.

Another type of fabric is the Gripper or Tufted Axminster (Fig. 6), in which the construction of the cloth is the same as the Spool Axminster, but the method of inserting the tufts is somewhat differ-

ent. This system is a cross between the Axminster and Jacquard weaving, as a Jacquard is used for selecting the threads required.

The yarn is placed in frames as in Wilton weaving, but in this case eight frames may be used as against five or six. One thread of colour from each frame is put into an upright carrier at the front of the loom, one above the other, the ends just protruding. The carriers, side by side across the loom, are raised to varying heights by the Jacquard, so that the required colour comes directly opposite to a "gripper". These grippers are shaped rather like a bird's head, the beak taking hold of the end opposite and pulling out a small tuft of yarn that is then cut from the main length. The grippers now swing down and insert the tufts into the carpet, the weft being passed across by a needle and binding the tufts into the back. In this process the length of pile is governed by the length of yarn that the gripper pulls out before it is cut off.

A third type of weaving is Chenille, in which there are two separate weaving processes. The first process makes the actual chenille and the second involves the weaving of the carpet proper.

CHENILLE

In Chenille weaving the warp consists of fine cotton threads, and the weft is the wool yarn that eventually is to become the pile of the carpet. The cotton threads are placed apart at intervals of roughly half-an-inch—according to the length of pile required—and the wool weft is passed from side to side of the loom by means of a shuttle, the cotton binding it together and making a loose, open fabric. The threads of weft are changed from one colour to another to fit into the design. The cloth is then put into a machine that cuts the wool weft midway between the cotton threads,

HOW THE PATTERN IS CONTROLLED

Fig. 5. *After the design has been punched out on to the cards by the card cutter, these are inserted into the machine to control the pattern woven by the spools. The cards are merely punched with holes at certain intervals to control the coloured threads.*

thus leaving long lengths of parallel tufts of wool in ladder formation, with the "rungs" bound in the middle instead of at the ends. These lengths of chenille "fur", as they are called, are steamed and passed over a grooved steam-heated cylinder. The purpose of this is to make all the tufts assume a U-shaped form, all being bound to one another by the cotton thread situated at the circular portion of the "U".

Lengths of this fur are now put into large shuttles and sent to the looms for the actual weaving of the carpet. Two shuttles are used: one carries a jute weft that makes the backing by crossing from one side of the loom four times; then the large shuttle crosses, carrying

the fur. The loom now stops while the weaver combs the fur up to the already woven carpet, and satisfies himself that the design is piecing together properly. The fur is held on to the backing by means of very fine cotton warps, that cross over it and are then bound into the back themselves. Great care is taken that these fine cotton threads are not cut or the pile will begin to come away from the back in strips.

By whichever process the carpet has been made, it is submitted to the final operation of finishing before it leaves the factory. In this process all the roughness left by the loom is removed, and everything generally is tidied up. For instance, occasionally an end breaks in the loom, with the result that there is a tuft of pile missing. The menders search all over the carpet for these faults, and sew in the colour where a tuft is out (Fig. 1). In the better qualities of Wilton there are sometimes knots of yarn showing on the back, so these are cut off and the back of the carpet is cleaned up. The carpet is then steamed in order to "burst" the yarn—that is, to loosen the twist to give a more even covering effect. At this stage some carpets—such as the lower qualities of Axminster, Grippers and Wiltons—are sized on the back to make them stiffer.

After steaming and sizing, the carpet is dried over steam-heated cylinders, then passed to the cropping machine. Here is a fluted cutting cylinder, very similar to that on a lawn-mower. The carpet passes under this cutter, sufficiently close to it to remove all the outstanding "whiskers" and fibres, any tiny irregularities on the pile being removed in the cropping. After this the carpet is examined very carefully for every possible flaw, and only those which are passed as perfect go through the last process of being measured. They are then sent to the warehouse for storage and distribution to the various retail firms as and when required.

TUFTED CARPETS

Fig. 6. In the Gripper carpet, small tufts of yarn are seized by the gripper from the frames and inserted into the carpet. The length of pile depends on the length of the tuft.

COINS

The Royal Mint. Gold, Silver and Bronze. Hardness of Alloys. Life of Coins.
Refining Processes. Melting and Assaying. Casting Bars and Ingots. Rolling
Out Bars into Metal Strip. Annealing. Coin Presses and Stamping Dies.
Weighing, Testing and Counting into Bags.

As everyone knows, British coins are made at the Royal Mint, a large building—or rather series of buildings—a few hundred yards to the north-east of the Tower of London, and built in 1810. Here most of the coinage of the British Empire is minted, and also the medals issued by the Navy, Army and Air Force and the medals of the Royal Societies. The "making of money" becomes a very prosaic and matter-of-fact operation, for the Mint is merely a metal-smelting factory allied to a specialised engineering shop. Metal is melted and coins stamped out on presses, very much in the same way as thousands of metal parts are made in engineering works in Birmingham or Sheffield. It is only the token value of the article which is produced that causes the processes and the materials which are involved to be so closely guarded.

COINS OF ALLOY

The coins normally made at the British Mint are gold, silver, and bronze, though in recent years very little gold coinage has been produced. Generally speaking, the value of the metal actually contained in coins is less than the face value of the coins, the difference being made up by some alloy. For example, in Great Britain, 1 oz. of alloy, containing actually ½ oz. of silver, is made into coins of a total value of 5s. 6d. irrespective of the price of silver bullion. In 1927 the average London price per standard ounce was 26d., and in 1937 it was 20d., showing a fall of 6d. per oz.,

despite which the nominal face values of silver coin remained unchanged. The difference between the values of the bullion and the coin goes to the State to cover the cost of manufacture of the coin, and any further profit ranks as revenue. The London Mint's profit on silver coinage in 1937–8 amounted to over £2,835,000.

The use of alloys in minting dates from the time of the Greeks, who coined not only pure gold and silver, but also electrum—an alloy of both. The Romans first added copper to their gold coinage, and later used base alloys in which there was only 2 per cent of gold and sometimes even less than that! The gold standard for coins in England was fixed in 1526 at $\frac{11}{12}$ or 916.6 (22 carats) fine, and remains the same today.

The silver standard is 925—that is 925 parts of silver in 1,000 parts—or 11 oz. 2 dwt. silver and 18 dwt. alloy. Although this standard dates from Saxon days, it has been reduced at various times. For instance, Henry VIII debased it first to 10 oz. silver and 2 oz. alloy, and later to 4 oz. silver and 8 oz. alloy. It was raised again to 925 by Elizabeth, but debased in 1920 to 500.

HARDENED BY COPPER

Although the Roman Emperors introduced copper into the gold coinage merely for the purpose of profit, copper in gold and in silver coin actually results in a greater hardness than that of coin of pure metal, thus enabling the coin to remain longer in circulation. As a general

MELTING SILVER IN GAS-FIRED FURNACES

Fig. 1. *Scene in the Royal Mint. Silver ingots or worn coins are placed in the crucibles and the molten metal is poured into moulds to form bars for rolling into strip.*

rule it has been found that large silver coins of 925 standard will wear well for about forty years, but the serviceable life of small coins is somewhat shorter.

Nearly all copper coins contain tin and zinc, generally in the proportion of about 95 per cent copper, 4 per cent tin, and 1 per cent zinc. In some countries nickel and aluminium are also alloyed with copper—this is the case with the francs of Belgium and France, which were formerly made of silver.

Gold and silver cannot be used just as they come from the mines, but must be refined before being ready for minting. Refining, which is not generally done by the Mint but by outside firms, consists of extracting the impurities from the nuggets and gold dust of the mines. In gold the chief impurity is silver, usually present to the extent of about 8 per cent, with other metals to the extent of 2 per cent. The metal is generally refined by the chlorine process,

invented in 1869 in Australia, in which chlorine gas is passed through molten gold. The gas is absorbed by the silver that is present as an impurity, and in this way silver chloride is formed. This is skimmed from the surface of the metal, the other metallic impurities being similarly chloridized. In the United States mints most of the gold is refined by the electrolytic process, in which plates of the impure metal forming the anode are immersed in acid. The passage of an electric current deposits pure gold on the cathode plates.

In silver, the impurities may consist of small percentages of copper, gold, lead and other metals. This metal also may be refined by the electrolytic method; the anodes are formed by plates of silver suspended in porcelain vats containing nitric acid, and the pure metal is deposited on the cathode plates. The acid is agitated, as otherwise there is a tendency for the crystals of silver to form chains and join the cathode to the anode, thus causing short circuits.

After it has been refined, the pure metal, whether gold or silver, is cast into bars—gold bars weighing usually 400 oz. troy, and silver 1,000 oz.—and brought to the Mint. On arrival the ingots are carefully weighed and are then placed in the strong room. All metal issued is also very accurately weighed and must be accounted for— not one coin is allowed to be left unaccounted for—either in coin or scrap or even dust.

When minting the metal goes first to the melting room (Fig. 1) where it is melted down in gas-fired plumbago crucibles. At the Royal Mint these will hold 86 kilograms (2,750 oz.) of gold, or 188 kilograms (6,000 oz.) of silver. The necessary amount of metal to form the alloy is also included in the crucible which, when ready, is lifted by tongs suspended from an overhead electric crane and placed in a cradle by which it may be tilted for pouring. Before this is done a small quantity of the metal is extracted for assaying, for gold must conform within very close limits—2 parts per 1,000 above or below —to the 916.6 standard already mentioned. In the gold room there are eight furnaces and eight crucibles, each of which contains about £5,000 worth of gold. During the melting process the metal is carefully stirred in order to mix the copper with the gold.

The molten metal is then poured from the crucible into moulds, from which when cooled it is turned out as ingots. The moulds consist of iron bars held in a screw-press, and when this is released the moulds are dismantled, leaving the cast bars of metal about $\frac{1}{2}$ in. thick. Small pieces are cut from the first and the last bars for testing, and should it be found that the proportions are not correct the bars are melted down again.

ROLLING OUT THE BARS INTO STRIP

Fig. 2. *Gold or silver bars of the appropriate width, prepared in the melting room, are rolled out here into strips of the thickness of the coins to be manufactured.*

BULLION TO SPECIE: PROCESSES BY WHICH NATIVE

Fig. 3. *Taken first of all from the mine, indicated in the top left hand corner, silver ore is crushed, smelted and refined, in that order, until it is finally cast for convenience into ingots each weighing 1,000 Troy ounces. The succeeding stages follow in the order shown by the*

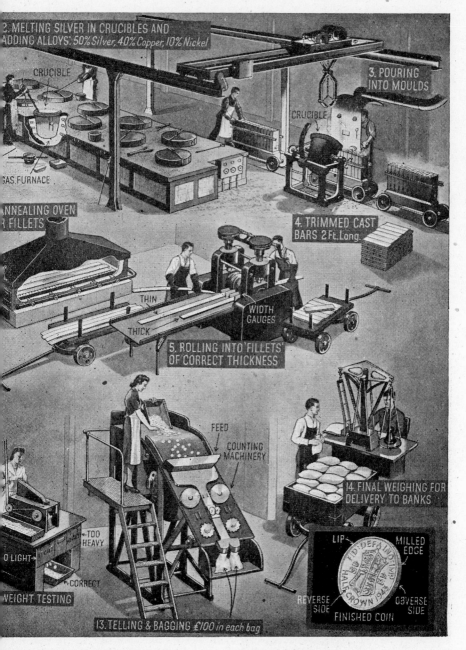

2. MELTING SILVER IN CRUCIBLES AND ADDING ALLOYS: 50% Silver, 40% Copper, 10% Nickel

CRUCIBLE

GAS FURNACE

3. POURING INTO MOULDS

CRUCIBLE

ANNEALING OVEN FILLETS

4. TRIMMED CAST BARS 2 Ft. Long.

THIN

WIDTH GAUGES

THICK

5. ROLLING INTO 'FILLETS' OF CORRECT THICKNESS

FEED

COUNTING MACHINERY

14. FINAL WEIGHING FOR DELIVERY TO BANKS

TOO HEAVY

TOO LIGHT

CORRECT

WEIGHT TESTING

LIP

MILLED EDGE

REVERSE SIDE

FID:DEF:IND:IMP HALF-CROWN 1945

OBVERSE SIDE

FINISHED COIN

13. TELLING & BAGGING £100 in each bag

SILVER IS TURNED INTO SHILLINGS AND HALF-CROWNS

numbers. The annealing or softening processes shown at 6 and 8 are necessary both for the purpose of stamping the design on the small circular blanks cut out by the machine at 7 and for rolling the bar castings into the original strip from which these blanks are cut.

E.T.T.S.—G*

They go next to the rolling room (Fig. 2), where they pass through a succession of steel rollers that thin them out by $\frac{1}{100}$ in. at each roll, until ultimately they become "fillets" about $1\frac{1}{2}$ in. in width and $\frac{1}{20}$ in. thick. The latter measurement must be correct within $\frac{1}{20000}$ in. because on its correctness depends the accuracy of the weight of the coin, the thickness of the fillet being that of the coin that is to be minted from it. When this rolling process is completed the strips are inspected by the "tryer", who determines whether they are of the correct thickness.

The next process is to blank out disks (Fig. 3 (7)). This operation is done by a machine that punches out blanks in pairs at the rate of 150 per minute, the metal not used being returned to be melted down. Two cylindrical cutters force the metal through holes of the requisite size, the strip of metal being

DIE-SINKING ROOM
Fig. 4. *Machine for forming the dies that impress the design on the coins.*

moved into position after each punch ready for the following punch (Fig. 6). The blanks are next taken to a machine for "marking"—the operation in which a rim is rolled on them. The effect of this rim is to protect the coin from wear and so give it a longer life. Marking is done by passing the blanks between the face of a revolving wheel and a fixed block carrying a groove, the distance between which is slightly less than the diameter of the blank.

Next comes the annealing, or softening, for which the blanks are placed in powdered charcoal and passed through a furnace (Fig. 3(8)) for about three hours.

They are then "blanched" by passing them through a furnace, in which they are heated to a dull red. In the process they become blackened by the formation of oxide of copper, but this is removed by passing them through a solution of sulphuric acid (Fig. 3(9))

STAMPING PRESS
Fig. 5. *This machine impresses the design for coin or medal on the blank disks.*

STAMPING OUT BLANK DISKS FROM STRIP METAL

Fig. 6. *One of the machines used for cutting out the small circular disks which are eventually to become coins. The disks are formed in pairs by cylindrical cutters at the rate of 150 per minute. A strip of metal can be seen being fed into the cutter by the operator.*

A CORNER OF THE COINING ROOM AT THE ROYAL MINT

Fig. 7. *A number of coin presses of various sizes are shown here. They are capable of striking coins of any denomination at the rate of 100 to 120 per minute.*

This is done on presses each of which imprints the design from a die with a 30-ton blow (Figs. 5 and 7). The dies are of hardened steel (Fig. 4), and are made from the original design reproduced in relief and copied in miniature by a reducing machine. Such a die will strike 50,000 coins before wearing out.

In the striking operation, one die is fixed and the other is in the movable part of the press. Between them is a collar milled inside—which is used for all coins except the crown and the 3d. bit. The blank is automatically fed into the lower die, and when it is encircled by the collar the upper die descends, imprinting the design on the obverse and reverse, at the same time forcing the edge into the collar by which it is given the familiar milled edge. The coin then moves down a channel. The operation is done by presses that are either hand-fed or automatic, with a capacity for dealing with 100 coins per minute.

Each coin is then weighed by delicate balances contained in glass cases, any coins that are of incorrect weight being automatically rejected and returned to the melting pot. So delicate are these automatic balances that they will reject any coins that are too light or too heavy within very fine limits—to within .17 of a grain in the case of sovereigns. Whilst 10 per cent of gold coins may be rejected, silver rejects are generally below 1 per cent. The coins are then tested for soundness by "ringing", each being dropped on to a steel slab. Finally they are examined by eye as they pass along on travelling belts (Fig. 3(11)).

Contrary to a general idea, the English penny of 1864 is not of special value. Some years ago a story was circulated that in 1864 gold was accidentally mixed with the bronze coinage, and the story is varied only by the mention of different years. An official statement had to be issued to correct this false impression.

TWO OF THE TELLING MACHINES AT THE MINT

Coins are always counted automatically at the Royal Mint. As shown in Fig. 3 (13) the coins slide down through the counting machinery and fall into bags at the bottom. In the foreground above can be seen stacks of bagged coins awaiting dispatch to the banks.

ARTIFICIAL SILK IN THE MAKING

Fig. 1. *Few people would recognize artificial silk, or rayon, in the powdered form shown above. This powder which looks like bread-crumbs is made from material known as alkali cellulose, which, in turn, is simply wood-pulp which has been steeped in caustic soda.*

206

ARTIFICIAL SILK

Cellulose, Common Basis of Rayon. Mystery of the Silkworm. Solid and Liquid Cellulose. Viscose Process. Stages in Manufacture. Pressing Wood-Pulp. Dissolving Impurities. Chemical Changes. Grinding and Churning. Maturing. Spinning. Winding into Hanks and Dyeing.

WE have all had experience of stringy cabbage, of unchewable lettuce, of turnips and beet-roots that will never boil tender. Our trouble with these disagreeable vegetables is due to the fact that for purposes of their own they have been very busily engaged in turning starch and sugar into that remarkable and useful substance, cellulose.

Cellulose is one of the great puzzles of organic chemistry, as the branch of chemistry which investigates the composition of living organisms is called. The organic chemist knows what it is made of, and the botanist knows why it is made; but neither can tell us exactly *how* it is made. All green plants take water, containing certain chemical salts, from the soil, and carbon dioxide from the air. In some miraculous way not yet understood, minute green bodies called chloroplasts contained in the cells of the leaves call sunlight into partnership for the manufacture of everything contained in the plant. Starch, sugar, cellulose, gums, resin, pectin (the stuff that makes jams and jellies set) as well as the "alkaloids" such as quinine and strychnine, or the ethers and esters which give to plants their characteristic smells and tastes, are all made by the plant out of water and carbonic acid gas.

CELLULOSE AND THE TREE

There is no vegetable product more interesting or more useful to man than cellulose. It is the fibrous part of the plant, the woody tissue, immensely strong and resilient, and providing the framework which holds together the uncountable millions of fluid-containing cells. Nothing better illustrates the strength of cellulose fibres than a large tree. Think of a giant oak, holding out its mighty branches almost at right-angles to the trunk, in defiance of the storms of centuries. Wood consists of bundles of fibres held together by the strong electrical attraction existing between the cellulose molecules which form each individual fibre. These molecules have such a strong affinity for one another that they are almost as difficult to separate as the molecules in a piece of steel wire of equal thickness.

USES OF CELLULOSE

Man has made use of cellulose for many centuries—for instance, in the employment of building timber; but the modern chemist has provided a host of new cellulose products. About a hundred years ago a German chemist announced the discovery of gun-cotton, made by treating cotton with nitric and sulphuric acids, and so began the development of powerful high explosives based on nitro-cellulose. In 1855, a Mr. Parkes of Birmingham mixed gun-cotton with oils and camphor, and celluloid appeared. The main use of celluloid is for photographic film.

If celluloid could be rolled into thin transparent films, why might it not equally be forced through little holes to form fine threads? Many experimenters sought a practical answer to the question; but that practical answer had been worked out hundreds of thousands of years before by the silkworm and other silk-producing caterpillars. These creatures obtain cellulose from plants and dissolve it into a clear thin liquid which at once hardens when it is forced through their minute spinnerettes.

UNLIKE COTTON OR FLAX

The result is a very smooth cylindrical filament, entirely different from the flat, coarse fibres of cotton or flax, and much more desirable than those fibres for weaving into fine fabrics. But silk is rare and therefore costly. A cheap silk was a goal well worth striving for.

Now it must be said at once that, despite their apparent similarity, real silk is chemically a very different substance from man-made silk. We cannot copy the silkworm's process, for the simple reason that we have not yet discovered its secret. For that reason—though there are others too—it is better to speak of the silk substitute made in factories as rayon, the name given to it by the manufacturer, than as "artificial silk". The latter name, however, was given to it by Sir Joseph Wilson Swan, who invented a process for making cellulose threads as far back as 1883.

FIRST RAYON FABRIC

His interest in these threads lay in their use as suitable filament for his incandescent electric lamp, first publicly exhibited in 1878, a year before Edison patented in Britain the carbon filament lamp. But Mrs. Swan, charmed by the silky lustre of the fine cellulose threads, crocheted some of them into edgings for d'oyleys, and in so doing created the first rayon fabrics. The commercial production of nitro-cellulose yarn was begun a year or two later in France by Count Hilaire de Chardonnet, the well-known scientist and experimenter.

Today the rayon industry is of gigantic proportions and is steadily growing. All the world asks for rayon, a material at once soft and fine, with the sheen of silk but stronger and better in wear, and costing but a fraction of the price. It can be made from a variety of vegetable substances, converted by four or five distinct processes. Crude cellulose is not invariably the basis of rayon, for it can also be manufactured from the casein of milk; this method, however, is as yet very little used. Chemists find it easier, and a great deal cheaper, to undertake the entire conversion of the cellulose by artificial means than to let the cow do some of the work.

TRIUMPH OF RESEARCH

Each of the five processes is a triumph of chemical research and discovery. All of them require *solid* cellulose to be changed into a *liquid* and then, when the thread is formed, immediately changed once more into a solid. The problem is how to do this without destroying the long, chain-like cellulose molecules, whose affinity for one another must be preserved in order to give strength to the ultimate rayon threads.

The "viscose" process is that chiefly employed in Britain. Viscose rayon is directly descended from Swan's electric lamp experiments, and was developed from insignificant beginnings to the great industry of today by the energy and enterprise of the firm of Courtaulds.

Viscose manufacture begins a long way from the rayon factory (see Fig. 3). In Canada and Newfoundland hundreds of thousands of spruce and hemlock trees are felled during the winter months, when their life-processes are least active. Here is the stored cellulose, in a highly-concentrated and relatively pure state. The felled trees are hauled to the frozen rivers, accumulating in stupendous stacks upon the ice. With

SHEETS OF WOOD-PULP BEING TRIMMED TO SIZE

Fig. 2. *Canadian wood-pulp arrives at the factory in the form of sheets, resembling blotting paper, which are later turned into alkali cellulose and ground to powder.*

the spring comes the thaw, and on the released waters the trees begin their journey downstream to the pulping mills. This is where the lumber-jacks play their most spectacular rôle. It is their task to see that the logs, borne seawards in thousands, do not pile up in jams at the bends and rapids in the rivers and so hold up the steady flow.

At the mills the trees are stripped of bark and sawn into small logs, which are then submitted to machines which tear them to shreds. These huge pulping machines tower to three or four times the height of the men who work them. The logs, in a continuous flow, enter the machine at the top, to come under the influence of massive downward-moving chains. Each link of the chains is fitted

with a wedge-shaped projection which forces the logs against revolving grinders. The small fragments of wood which result from the milling are next boiled with chemicals to remove the resins, gums and impurities with which the pine trees are impregnated. Then they are washed, bleached and scoured again and again, until at last all that remains of the trees is a mass of pure cellulose fibres. When at last the sodden mass of pulp is sufficiently purified, it is dried by passing it over steam-heated cylinders and pressed into sheets, which are baled in hydraulic presses for convenience of transport to the rayon factory.

It might be supposed that in reducing hundreds and thousands of tree trunks to pulp by large-scale machinery it is

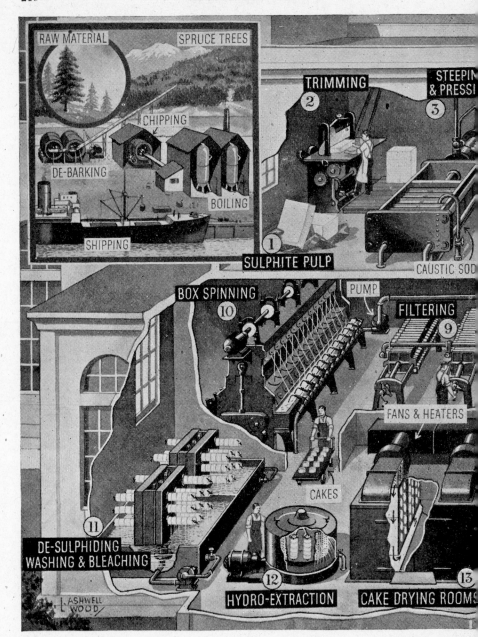

HOW ARTIFICIAL SILK STOCKINGS ARE MADE FROM

Fig. 3. *Logs arrive at the factory as sulphite pulp* (1) *which is trimmed* (2) *and turned into alkali cellulose* (3), *then ground* (4), *and churned into cellulose xanthate* (5). *This is now transformed into viscose* (6), *then ripened, evacuated and filtered* (7, 8, 9) *after which it is spun out into threads* (10). *Succeeding phases consist mainly of winding the threads into cakes*

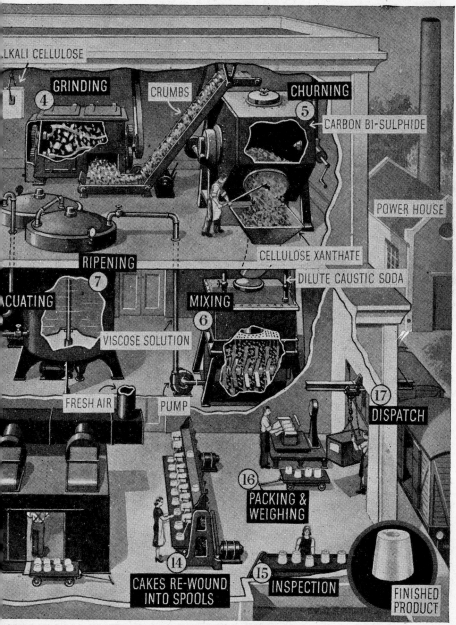

ALKALI CELLULOSE

GRINDING
4

CRUMBS

CHURNING
5

CARBON BI-SULPHIDE

POWER HOUSE

RIPENING
7

CELLULOSE XANTHATE

DILUTE CAUSTIC SODA

VACUATING

MIXING
6

VISCOSE SOLUTION

FRESH AIR

PUMP

17
DISPATCH

16
PACKING &
WEIGHING

14
CAKES RE-WOUND
INTO SPOOLS

15
INSPECTION

FINISHED
PRODUCT

SPRUCE LOGS GROWN IN CANADIAN FORESTS

for ease of cleansing, washing and drying (11, 12, 13) then rewinding the final spools (14) for inspection and packing (15, 16). From the finished product can be woven all the articles in general use. Two other methods of producing rayon are known as the cellulose acetate and cuprammonium processes, the former producing rayon of a very fine and silk-like quality.

impossible to exercise the exact control necessary for the making of fine chemicals. Here, one would think, the rough and ready methods of the backwoods must prevail. In actual fact the contrary is the case. The ultimate success of the rayon manufacture—the strength, fineness and softness of the yarn which the cellulose is to produce—depends very largely on control at the pulping mill. Every stage is watched and checked. The temperature and strength of the cleansing fluids are matters of great importance, and the chemists at the pulp mills must maintain over the ground-up trees as much care and exactitude as we normally expect from the dispensing chemist who makes up the doctor's prescriptions.

NURSING THE CELLULOSE

The care taken at the pulping mills to make sure of an exact standard of cellulose purity is of immense consequence throughout all the changes the cellulose must undergo. Once arrived at the rayon factory, the cellulose is guarded, nursed and cossetted as though the sheets—resembling thick white blotting paper (Fig. 2)—were composed of the rarest and most delicate fabrics instead of the fibres of disintegrated trees. In all the processes that are to follow, details of weight, time, temperature and so on will be tested time and time again. Even the amount of moisture in the air must be controlled from hour to hour.

The first step is to cut the sheets of cellulose to batches of a given weight and to "condition" them to a uniform content of moisture. These batches are then steeped in a "mercerising" bath of caustic soda—the wizard's bath which really begins the change from wood to silk-like threads. Caustic soda, a very strong alkali made from common salt and water by electrolysis, is used by hundreds of thousands of tons in many different industries. It is called "caustic" because it burns away and destroys animal and vegetable tissues. Despite the many purification processes the pulp has already undergone, it still contains much unwanted material. In the soda bath this is dissolved away, leaving only the pure cellulose, which now combines with the soda to form what is known as alkali cellulose. The tanks are fitted with hydraulic rams; and when the mercerising process is complete and the soda solution is drained off, the rams are brought into action and press out of the pulp sheets all but a carefully calculated proportion of moisture. When this has been done the sheets are removed to the "pfleiderers".

The pfleiderer may be likened to an overgrown relative of the domestic mincing machine. Large spiral blades revolving between serrated bars "mince" the pulp to a state resembling breadcrumbs (Fig. 1). The crumbs are shovelled into bins and taken to a ripening room, where under conditions of rigidly controlled temperature and humidity the mercerisation begun in the soda bath is carried a stage further. The next operation brings about the first fundamental change in the condition of the cellulose, which up to this point has remained recognisable as a mass of finely divided wood fibres. It has now to be converted to a completely different substance known as cellulose xanthate.

THE CHURNING PROCESS

The crumbs from the pfleiderers are taken to the churn room and poured into large hexagonal churns, where they are mixed with carbon disulphide, an extremely unpleasant chemical smelling of rotten eggs. It is made by burning carbon in sulphur vapour. Each atom of carbon combines with two atoms of sulphur, and the resultant product is carbon disulphide. In spite of its

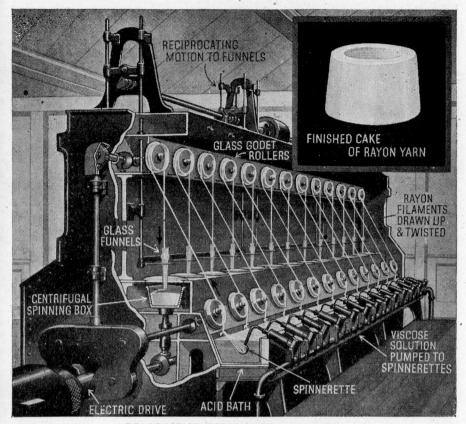

RECIPROCATING MOTION TO FUNNELS

FINISHED CAKE OF RAYON YARN

GLASS GODET ROLLERS

RAYON FILAMENTS DRAWN UP & TWISTED

GLASS FUNNELS

CENTRIFUGAL SPINNING BOX

VISCOSE SOLUTION PUMPED TO SPINNERETTES

SPINNERETTE

ELECTRIC DRIVE   ACID BATH

DIAGRAM OF TOPHAM BOX SPINNER

Fig. 4. *Liquid viscose is pumped to the spinnerettes and forced through tiny holes into an acid bath, where it solidifies and becomes rayon yarn ready for coiling.*

objectionable smell and high inflammability it is a very useful chemical, applied in many different industries. Even gardeners sometimes use it to kill moles, rabbits and mice by putting it in their runs. It works a miracle on the alkali cellulose in the churns, reducing the insoluble crumbs to a sticky orange mass soluble in water. This is cellulose xanthate. The discovery of this reaction was made by two English chemists, C. F. Cross and E. J. Bevan, in 1892. By this discovery Cross and Bevan made possible the viscose process, on which more than three-quarters of the total of the world's rayon production depends.

It is an easy step from cellulose xanthate to viscose. The sticky mass from the churns is transferred to drums fitted with paddles and is thoroughly mixed with water. The resulting viscose much resembles thin golden syrup. This syrupy stuff, however, is not yet fit to be made into rayon.

First it must be allowed to mature, for which purpose it is transferred to underground chambers of carefully regulated temperature, appropriately called "caves". While in the caves, where it remains for several days, a number of important things are done to the viscose. The batches from the different mixing drums are blended together to make sure that the product is absolutely uniform. Then the viscose is filtered—not once, but again and again by being passed through several thicknesses of finely woven cloth and through thick pads of wadding. It is also necessary to make sure that the viscose is entirely free from bubbles of air or gas, and it is therefore passed through pipes in which a high vacuum is maintained. When all these things have been done the treacly fluid is at last ready to be spun into threads of rayon.

Perhaps the actual process of spinning may be made clearer if we imagine that we are allowed to handle some of the viscose for ourselves. Suppose we pour a little stream of the syrupy stuff into a glass of water; the only thing that happens is that it is thinned, just as treacle or honey would be. But if, instead of pure water, our glass contains a solution of dilute acid, then, when we pour in a thin stream of viscose a very remarkable change takes place: the viscose at once coagulates and in a very short time becomes solid. How is this change actually brought about?

STRENGTH OF CELLULOSE

At the beginning of this chapter we referred to the strength of cellulose fibres. Now this strength is due to the powerful mutual attraction of the molecules. In preparing the viscose the cellulose fibres have become very finely divided—so finely, in fact, that not even the most powerful microscope can reveal their presence. The perfectly translucent syrup is in reality composed of vast numbers of cellulose molecules suspended in an alkaline solution. It is the alkali which keeps them apart; if the alkali is removed the molecules will rush together and cling to one another with their old tenacity. The alkali might be washed out with water; but a much

simpler method is to neutralise it—to cancel it out—with acid.

To make a thread of rayon the finely filtered viscose must be forced through a tiny hole in imitation of the method used by the spider and the silkworm. The thread-making apparatus used in the rayon factory is, in fact, called a spinnerette (Fig. 4). Each spinnerette is about the size of a small thimble and is worth more than its weight in gold, being made quite frequently of an alloy of gold and platinum.

MICROSCOPIC MEASUREMENTS

The size of the "jets" or holes in the head of the spinnerette is microscopically small; their number varies according to the number of filaments of rayon required in the yarn to be spun. There may be as many as 500, though 200, or even fewer, are more usual; and if you can imagine making 200 separate holes in a thimble-head you may have some idea of the size of each hole. Just as there are different "counts" or thicknesses of cotton and silk yarns, so also different counts, called deniers, of rayon yarn are needed. Rayon locknit underwear is generally made of 60 denier yarns, and stockings of finer yarns, while furnishing fabrics go up to 300 deniers and more.

The spinning-room at the rayon factory houses some of the most ingenious and delicate machinery ever invented (Fig. 5). The viscose comes in pipes from the filters to the spinning machines, each of which operates many spinnerets. The extreme delicacy of the machines may be imagined from the fact that they are making fibres so slender that they are hardly visible, yet making them at the rate of thousands of miles a day. A pump forces a constant stream of viscose through the minute jets of the spinnerettes, from which it issues into an acid bath, there to solidify into as many

SPINNING ROOM IN RAYON FACTORY

Fig. 5. *On the left can be seen a spinning machine of the type illustrated in diagram form in Fig. 4. As the liquid viscose solidifies into threads in the acid bath the threads are wound into rolls in spinning pots. The operator in the foreground has just taken one of these pots from the machine to remove the rayon whilst the man next him is replacing one. Snow-white rolls of rayon are seen on the tables, and on the trolley to the right.*

parallel filaments as there are holes in the spinneret. The reason for the meticulous filtration the viscose undergoes now becomes clear. The smallest speck of matter, or even an air-bubble, would block the tiny holes, causing a break in the continuity of the thread and a weak place in the yarn into which the filaments have to be spun.

TWISTING THREADS INTO YARN

We have reached the stage when from each of the spinnerets on the spinning machine—perhaps a hundred of them—there is formed in the acid bath a group of continuous filaments, all lying close together in a little bundle. With a pin and a magnifying glass you can detach one of these single fibres from any rayon stuff, although you can scarcely see it. Before any use can be made of them they must be *twisted* into yarn.

The next process, then, is to twist a group of filaments into yarn. In front of each spinnerette there is a glass roller, over which the filaments are drawn (Fig. 4). Next they drop down a glass funnel which rises and falls in front of the roller. The funnel leads to a revolving cylinder known as the spinning pot or "box". Now, since the pot is revolving quickly the filaments are brought under centrifugal force; they are flung against the side of the pot, becoming twisted at the same time. The result is that the pot fills itself, not with disconnected weak parallel fibres, but with strong continuous yarn. When the pot is taken from the machine it contains a cylindrical "cake" of rayon, hollow in the centre (Fig. 5). These cakes are removed to cabinets, wherein they are "conditioned" to harden and toughen the yarn. The next thing is to unwind the cakes, the thread of which they are composed being rewound into hanks, this being the easiest form in which the rayon can undergo the subsequent processes (Fig. 7).

It must not be supposed that the brand-new rayon thread is yet ready for the weaver or the hosiery manufacturer. In every factory aiming at a first-class product immense pains are taken to ensure that the rayon is in the best possible condition for dyeing in any one of the huge range of delicate shades demanded by the market. For this it must be absolutely free from traces of chemicals and bleached to snow-white purity (Fig. 6). After hanking, the rayon yarn is washed, then dried in ovens. Next it is washed again, before being dosed with bleaching solution. But it is not even now ready by any means! Every trace of bleaching solution must be removed (or, more correctly, neutralised) by further chemical treatment; then the excess bleach-neutraliser must also be removed by washing in soapy water—a simple process which is nevertheless carried out with the greatest care. Finally, the washed hanks are wrapped in clean cloths, deprived of nearly all their moisture in centrifugal hydro-extractors like those used for drying clothes at the laundry, and then "dried off" in steam-heated chests. The rayon is then ready for the dye-works.

DYED RAYON

More than three-quarters of British rayon output is made by the viscose process just described. A large proportion of the output is used by locknit and stocking manufacturers in the continuous thread yielded by the dyed hanks. Much is also woven on looms made for the purpose. But as a consequence of the great demand for all kinds of fabrics consisting either in part or entirely of rayon it is also necessary to produce what are known as staples. These are short lengths of rayon fibre suitable for spinning and weaving by the usual textile machinery, either as pure rayon or mixed with cotton, silk or

EXAMINING SNOW-WHITE HANKS OF RAYON FOR FLAWS

Fig. 6. *The photograph shows a corner of the inspection room of a rayon factory, where girls examine the finished hanks of artificial silk. The hanks are bleached to dazzling whiteness, this being necessary so that they can be dyed in the many well-known delicate shades.*

REWINDING RAYON YARN INTO HANKS

Fig. 7. *The spools of yarn can be seen on the shelves at the feet of the operators. The winding frames above are very similar in style to the usual home wool-winder.*

wool. The short rayon staple is made in exactly the same way as the continuous yarn up to the point of spinning. Instead of being twisted into a thread the filaments issuing from the jet are gathered together immediately they have hardened in the acid bath. The mass of parallel filaments is then automatically cut to predetermined lengths.

The relatively small proportion of rayon not made from viscose is produced by two methods known respectively as the cellulose acetate and cuprammonium processes. In these processes the cellulose is reduced to a clear fluid by chemical solvents and forced through fine jets. The actual spinning is, however, entirely different from that for viscose. In the cellulose acetate process the spinning machines consist of tall chambers in which currents of hot air circulate. The filaments from the jets harden in the hot air and fall to the bottom of the chambers, after which they are wound on bobbins. Rayon made in this way has a very soft and silk-like "feel" and can be woven into some of the loveliest fabrics.

We all want "man-made silk", as the Chinese call it, and it is safe to predict that alone and in combination with other Textile materials it will be immensely popular in the future. Even today the demand for rayon throughout the world is enormous, and is still increasing. New materials create new markets. How much is used may be judged from the fact that in a typical rayon spinning room the thread produced in a single hour would completely girdle the earth.

OPTICAL GLASS

Accuracy of Workmanship. Eye and Camera. Defective Vision. Spherical and Cylindrical Lenses. High Quality Glass. Grinding and Polishing. Cutting the Edges, Bifocal Lenses. Invisible Eye Lenses of the Future.

IF you take a piece of string about four yards long, fix one end to a table with a drawing pin and attach a pencil to the other end, you can describe a circle with a diameter of eight yards. The curve of the circumference will be so slight that a two-inch segment of it will look like a straight line.

Now imagine the surface of a piece of glass ground and polished to fit that segment, and you have some idea of the accurate workmanship necessary in the making of an ordinary spectacle lens.

The human eye is an extremely delicate and accurate form of camera. At the front it has a lens and an iris diaphragm, and at the back is a sensitive screen, on which the lens focuses a picture of whatever you are looking at (Fig. 4D).

But in one important respect, the eye differs from a camera. Most cameras can be focused by altering the distance

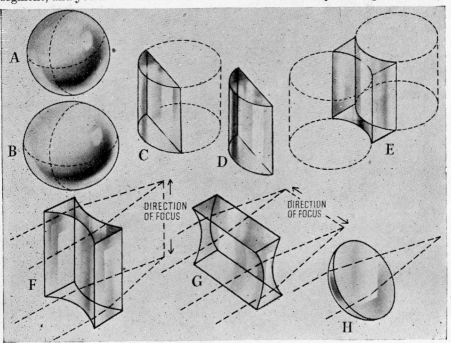

CYLINDRICAL AND SPHERICAL LENSES

Fig. 1. (A) *Normal cornea—perfectly regular curvature.* (B) *Astigmatic cornea—curvature slightly greater vertically than horizontally.* (C and D) *Convex cylindrical lens.* (E) *Concave cylindrical lens.* (F and G) *The focus of a cylindrical lens is a line whose direction depends upon the position in which the lens is held.* (H) *The focus of a spherical lens is a point. Unlike the focus of a cylindrical lens, it is not affected by rotation of the lens.*

POLISHING GROUND LENSES
Fig. 2. *This is done by machines which are fed continually with rouge and water.*

between the lens and the screen or plate. The eye cannot change its length in this way. Its normal length from back to front is about 23 millimetres—a little under an inch. The lens has a great range of focus and, when the eye is normal in size, can bring into clear vision objects at all distances from a few inches to many miles away.

Unfortunately, the eyes of some people are not normal in length; they may be a fraction of an inch too short or too long. These people have defective vision, because the focusing power of the lenses in their eyes is insufficient to compensate for this increased or reduced length. When the eyes are too long (Fig. 4c) it is difficult to bring distant objects into focus; and the person concerned is then said to be suffering from myopia, or short sight. When the eyes are too short (Fig. 4b) distant objects can be seen quite clearly but near vision is blurred and close work is difficult. This is called hypermetropia, or long sight.

As everybody knows, both these forms of faulty vision can be corrected by the use of spectacles containing lenses of a strength exactly sufficient to counteract the effects of the eye's abnormal shape. Such lenses are called "spherical", because their surfaces are ground to curves which are segments of spheres: that is, they are like slices cut from the surface of a huge glass globe. Spherical lenses may be convex—curving outwards from the edge to the centre; or concave—curving inwards. Convex lenses correct long sight, and concave short sight (Fig. 1).

There is also a third form of defective vision called astigmatism. This is due, not to a fault in the shape of the eye as a whole, but to a slightly distorted curvature in the transparent part of the front of the eye, known as the cornea. This should be perfectly spherical, but sometimes it is not. Its curvature in one

LENS BLANKS TAKING SHAPE
Raw optical glass being roughed down to correct curve on a rotating tool.

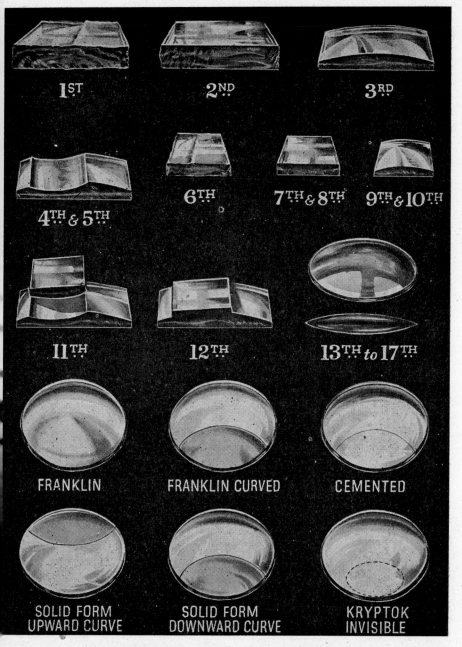

HOW MODERN INVISIBLE FUSED BIFOCAL LENSES ARE MADE

Fig. 3. *The numbered stages show the process of fusing two pieces of glass of different densities into one solid lens which can be used either for distant vision or close work. The invisible solid lens has evolved from the joined bifocals shown in the lower part.*

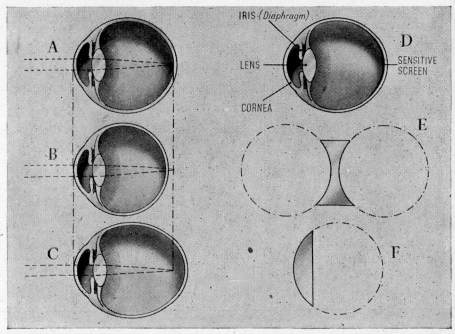

SHORT EYES RESULT IN LONG SIGHT, LONG EYES CAUSE SHORT SIGHT

Fig. 4. (A) *Normal eye;* (B) *Eye too short=hypermetropia or long sight, corrected by convex lens "F";* (C) *Eye too long=myopia or short sight, corrected by concave lens "E";* (D) *Diagram of eye. The lens, it will be noted, is placed well back from the surface.*

direction is slightly greater than that in the direction at right angles; instead of being quite round, it is very slightly spoon-shaped (Fig. 1B). For the correction of this condition it is necessary to use a lens known as a "cylinder" because it resembles a slice cut down the side of a very large glass rod or pillar. Such a lens has a focus in only one of 180 possible positions, and its usefulness in a pair of spectacles entirely depends upon the accuracy with which it is placed in that position relative to the eye for which it is prescribed (Fig. 1F and G).

When it is realised that nearly every person who needs to use spectacles regularly, whether for short or long sight, also suffers from some degree of astigmatism and therefore requires lenses ground to a spherical curve on one side and a cylindrical curve on the other, it is easy to see how precisely accurate must be the workmanship which goes into a pair of glasses.

Indeed, the glass used for optical purposes is very difficult to produce satisfactorily. Not only must there be no defects, such as bubbles, in it, but the glass itself must be perfectly homogeneous—that is, quite free from internal irregularities of texture or composition, which, though invisible to the naked eye, would nevertheless affect performance. To express this scientifically: the optical constant and refractive index of the glass must be the same throughout, as otherwise the rays passing through the lens will be subjected to dispersion, and every object seen through it will be distorted.

Only the purest materials must be used, and these must be ground to extreme fineness and very thoroughly mixed before melting. The melting process, by which the powdered silicates and other substances become glass by subjection to extreme heat, is done in pots which are moulded of the purest fireclay obtainable, as they must be quite free from any impurities that might melt and mix with the glass when heated. These pots, containing the powdered raw material of optical glass, are heated uniformly—top, bottom and sides—and the white-hot liquid in them is stirred frequently so as to mix the components thoroughly and make the mass as uniform as possible throughout.

But the most difficult process is that of cooling the glass after it has been heated sufficiently, because it is during the process of cooling, or "annealing", as it is called, that the glass is most likely to develop the internal stresses and warpings which would destroy its usefulness for optical purposes. The more slowly and steadily this cooling process takes place, the less likely are these stresses to occur. Actually the process takes days, and is carefully controlled by means of thermometers so that a steady rate of cooling is maintained for the whole period. The melting pots can be used only once, as the glass usually welds itself to them at the sides which, therefore, have to be broken away before the cold glass can be removed.

The slabs of glass are then broken into lumps for testing. The standard required is very high; indeed, from each pot of glass four-fifths are usually discarded as not sufficiently pure. The selected pieces are then re-annealed

and ground to the required shape for the manufacture of optical lenses. These are known as "blanks". Those which will eventually become spectacles are roughly square in shape and perfectly flat on both sides; they vary in thickness from one- to three-sixteenths of an inch. In this form they are sent by the glass manufacturers to the firms which specialise in lens grinding (Fig. 7).

The automatic machines used for grinding the surfaces of these blanks to the required spherical curvatures consist essentially of a mushroom-shaped, power-driven grinding tool set vertically in a large cylindrical trough. A steel disk, having its under surface accurately shaped to the curve which the lens surface will eventually take, is attached to a hinged steel rod fitted across the top of the trough, so that the curved surface of the disk, which is covered with felt or wash-leather, can be lowered on to the revolving tool (Fig. 5).

A number of lens blanks are cemented

CEMENTING OPTICAL GLASS

Canada balsam is used as cement when joining the two sections of bifocal lenses. Cleanliness in the use of this adhesive material is of utmost importance.

on to the mushroom-headed tool with pitch, and the fabric on the upper tool is impregnated with powdered emery mixed with water, and lowered on to the surface of the blanks. These are then set revolving at a high speed until, under the pressure of the upper tool, they gradually take its curvature. The method of grinding cylindrical lenses is similar, save that instead of revolving the tool oscillates.

The operation of grinding leaves the lenses with a matt surface, like ground glass; and they must next be polished with finer and finer grades of rouge until they are completely transparent and free from surface scratches. Polishing machines operate in the same manner as grinding machines; but the process must be very carefully controlled (Fig. 2).

When the blanks have been ground and polished on one side, they are gently heated to remove them from the pitch-covered tool, turned over and ground and polished on the other side. They are then ready for edging, so that they can be fitted into frames.

Every lens has what is known as an "optical centre". This is a point at the exact middle of the surface curve—the part where, in a convex lens, the glass is thickest; and in a concave lens where it is thinnest. It is very important to the wearer of spectacles that the optical centres of his lenses should be dead opposite the centre of his pupils. If they are not, the lenses will cause strain to the eye muscles, and their effect upon the vision will be a bad one.

Before lens blanks can be cut to shape, therefore, they have to be centred (Fig. 6). Special appliances have been invented to perform this operation. The machine is fitted with an eye-piece, through which the lens cutter looks at a geometrical design of crossed

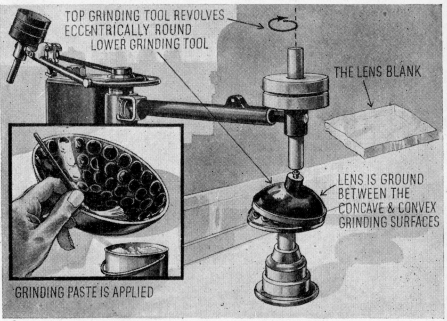

TOP GRINDING TOOL REVOLVES ECCENTRICALLY ROUND LOWER GRINDING TOOL

THE LENS BLANK

LENS IS GROUND BETWEEN THE CONCAVE & CONVEX GRINDING SURFACES

GRINDING PASTE IS APPLIED

METHOD OF GRINDING A LENS TO SHAPE

Fig. 5. *Lens blanks are cemented on to the lower mushroom-headed tool with pitch and are ground with powdered emery and water between the concave and convex surfaces.*

lines, so designed that it is distorted by the slightest displacement from the centre of the lens under observation, which is clipped into place on an adjustable stand. When the operator is satisfied that the lens blank is accurately centred, he operates a diamond cutting tool which describes a deep cut to the required size and .shape, at the correct distance from the lens centre.

The blank is then removed, the rough edges are tapped or chipped away, and it is ready for the edge-finishing machine, which smoothes and polishes the edge, giving it either a flat surface or a bevelled one, according to whether it is to be used in the rimmed or rimless variety of spectacles.

LENS BEING CENTRED ON EDGE-CUTTING TOOL
Fig. 6. *The image of a light bulb is viewed in the lens, which is centred when the image remains stationary.*

An edging machine is a large, automatically propelled grindstone made, usually, of very fine carborundum. The lens is held against the surface of the stone in a slowly rotating "former". Attached to this former is a metal template of the exact size and shape of the finished lens, which acts as a cam and imparts a rocking motion to the former as the grindstone revolves. The result of this motion is to press the lens against the stone, or withdraw it, so that as the grinding goes on it assumes the shape required—round, or oval, or part round and part oval—and is prevented from becoming smaller than the spectacle frame into which it will be fitted. There are, of course, standard sizes and shapes for all types of spectacles; and the metal frames of the spectacles, as well as the lens-formers, are made to these shapes and sizes.

At about the age of forty, even those who have hitherto needed no glasses

at all begin to want their assistance for reading and close work. This is because, at that age, the lens of the eye begins to lose its muscular resilience and cannot any longer make all the effort required for focusing nearby objects. This slight stiffening process increases yearly until about the age of sixty-five.

The condition, quite normal and healthy, is known as presbyopia, and it is corrected by suitable spectacles containing spherical lenses; these must be increased slightly in strength every couple of years or so, to make up for the stiffening of muscles in the internal eye.

These lenses do not, however, affect the wearer's ordinary vision. That is to say if he has needed spectacles for long sight, short sight or astigmatism earlier in life, he will still need their aid, and the strength of the "presbyopic correction", as it is technically called, must be added to that of the lenses hitherto used. This means that the person con-

GRINDING LENSES BY THE DOZEN

Fig. 7. *A series of grinding heads arranged conveniently along a bench. Two of the concave covers belonging to the upper part of the tools can be seen turned upside down.*

cerned now needs two different kinds of spectacles: one pair for distant vision and another for close work.

At one time, there was no alternative to having two pairs of spectacles in these circumstances; but some years ago opticians invented methods of combining two pairs of spectacles in one. They made lenses which had the top half suitable for distant vision and the lower half for reading.

Several different methods of achieving this result were adopted, only two of which are in general use today. The first and simpler method is to grind lenses to the strength required for distant vision in the ordinary way, then to make small, half-moon-shaped, wafer-thin lenses curved to the extra strength required for reading, and cement these wafers with Canada balsam to the lower half of the main lenses. This method has one great disadvantage from the point of view of the wearer. The edge of the wafer lens tends to get darkened into a line where dust settles on it, and this dark line in front of the eye is both unsightly and confusing to vision.

Research went on for a very long time before scientists discovered a way of making the bifocal lenses now in most general favour (Fig. 3). In these, the lenses are combined by welding into one piece of glass. There is no cementing of one piece on to another, nor is there any dividing line between the distance and reading strengths; indeed, without special knowledge an observer would not know that a person wearing lenses of this type had "bifocals" at all. The possibility of constructing these lenses depends on the optical properties of different kinds of glass, which vary in what is technically called their "refractive index". This means that if two lenses are ground to exactly the same surface curvature, one lens being made of crown glass and the other of flint, one will have a higher focusing power than the other.

Taking advantage of this peculiar property of different kinds of glass, expert lens workers developed an extremely ingenious idea. First, they made an ordinary spectacle lens of crown glass. Into the lower half of it they ground and polished a depression of carefully calculated curvature. Then they took a small blank of flint glass, and ground on one surface a convex curve which would precisely fit into the depression in the larger lens of crown glass. Next, by the application of heat, the two glasses were welded together; and finally, the whole composite surface was re-ground and polished. The result was a single piece of glass of uniform surface curvature, in which the lower part had more power than the other.

Of course, many unsuccessful experiments had to be made before dual-strength lenses of this kind became a practical proposition; and the most abstruse mathematical calculations had to be performed, to determine what degree of curvature at the welded surfaces of the two kinds of glass would enable the lens-makers to produce any required variation in optical strength between the two parts of the "fused"

CHECKING THE CURVE OF A POLISHED LENS

This is done by means of a test-plate. Each lens is polished true to its required curve to within limits approximating to the five-hundred thousandth part of an inch.

lens. But all that was merely a matter of time; and today, fused bifocals are worn by a great many people.

Crown and flint glass are not the only kinds used nowadays for lens manufacture. Some years ago the world-famous scientist, Sir William Crookes, discovered how glass could be impregnated with certain chemical substances which, while not affecting the transparency of lenses, would prevent certain chemical rays of light, irritating to the eye, from passing through them.

Optical glass is used in many ways, in telescopes, microscopes and other scientific instruments, but the processes are much the same, save where the lens becomes so large, as in the case of the giant telescope fitted in Mount Wilson Observatory, that special machinery has to be invented so as to deal with it.

But the very last word in optical invention is a lens so made that it fits over the curved front surface of the eye underneath the eyelids so that the wearer does not appear to be using glasses at all.

Already this type of lens is in use. It is an immense boon, of course, to such people as actors and actresses of the film and stage, for to them the wearing of spectacles is sometimes a disadvantage of a very serious kind; but it will probably be a long while before aids to vision of this kind come into general use. They have to be made with extreme care, and consequently are expensive; and few people can manage to use them for more than two or three hours at a time without feeling some irritation from their contact with the extremely sensitive front surface of the eyeball.

MOUNTING THE FINISHED LENS

All components are burnished into the cells and are made to revolve true to the optical axis of the lens. In the foreground can be seen some of the finished work.

PAINTS AND VARNISHES

Natural and Chemical Pigments. Crushing and Grinding. Levigation Process.
Opacity. White Oxides. Exterior and Interior Qualities. Colour Pigments. Oils
and Varnishes, Terebenes and Driers. Stoving Method. Oil-bound Distempers.

ALTHOUGH paint in some form or another enters everybody's domestic or commercial life, it must be agreed that the product is something of a mystery to the average man in the street.

Considerable progress has been made during the last decade in paints and varnishes both for the preservation and decoration of buildings and for industrial finishing. Most of this progress can be attributed to the efforts of those chemists and technologists who have done so much to please the tastes of the artistically minded and to develop materials which satisfy the needs of modern mass production methods.

Before proceeding to consider from what materials and by what methods the product is derived, we must get a clear picture in our minds of what paint is. All types of paint consist of dry pigments suspended in some suitable liquid, commonly referred to as the vehicle or medium. It is from the pigment that opacity and variation of shades are obtained; by the use of various types of liquid and different percentages of pigment, paint can be produced to meet almost every industrial demand.

NATURAL AND CHEMICAL PIGMENTS

Pigments can be divided into two main groups; (a) natural or mineral pigments, which exist in nature and require only mining and mechanical refining to make them suitable for use in the paint works; (b) those that are chemically prepared and do not exist

naturally in a "ready for use" form

Into class (a) fall the following, which are usually referred to as earth colours: yellow ochres, raw sienna, raw umber, vandyke brown and red oxides of iron.

By heating raw sienna and raw umber we get burnt sienna and burnt umber. Likewise the red oxides can be varied in shade by heat treatment, and although by this treatment a slight chemical change is undergone, for all practical purposes the products are still regarded as natural earth colours.

CRUSHING AND GRINDING

The next pigments in this class are those known as extenders, such as barytes, whiting, china clay, silica and others. Although these do not, by themselves, possess opacity, they play an important part in the dried film.

When natural pigments are extracted from the earth they are in a crude state and need refining, and the method most commonly employed is that of grinding and levigating. In the first process the crude material is broken up in a crusher (Figs. 1 and 2), and roughly powdered in an edge runner (Fig. 3), in which a heavy roller revolves in a circular pan; the particles of pigment in the machine are reduced in size by the friction which occurs between the roller and the base of the pan. The grinding surfaces may be made of steel or granite, according to the type of material being handled.

The material is then levigated (Fig. 3). It is fed into a stream of water and allowed to settle in tanks at various stages in its traverse. Naturally the

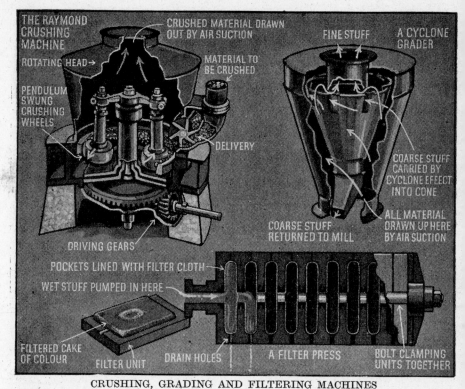

CRUSHING, GRADING AND FILTERING MACHINES

Fig. 1. (*Top, left*) *a crushing machine with pendulum-swung crushing wheels;* (*top, right*) *an air grader for dry powders;* (*bottom*) *a filter unit for wet ground pigments.*

texture of the material varies according to the position of the particular tank in which it settles, the finest product being that which settles in the last tank. The water from the tanks is then removed and the pigment which has settled is filtered and dried in an oven; it is then ground once more in an edge runner and is ready for marketing.

The chemical pigments include all the very important white pigments used in the paint industry. Perhaps first in importance is white lead (Fig. 4), vast quantities being used for all forms of exterior work. Although this has the disadvantage of being poisonous, it has nevertheless remained popular as it is very durable when used in paint. The dried film in which it is incorporated is

found to retain its elasticity and, therefore, does not become brittle. This results in a film which, when subjected to extremes of humidity and temperature, is able to withstand the varying degrees of expansion and contraction which always occur on exposure. The only objection which may be made to white lead is that since it does not harden to the same extent as some other white pigments, the surface tends to accumulate dust from the atmosphere.

Zinc oxide (Fig. 5) is another white pigment used in very large quantities, particularly in gloss paints. One reason for this is that the pigment tends to have a hardening effect upon the paint film; it also provides a paint possessing good flow. Owing to this hardening

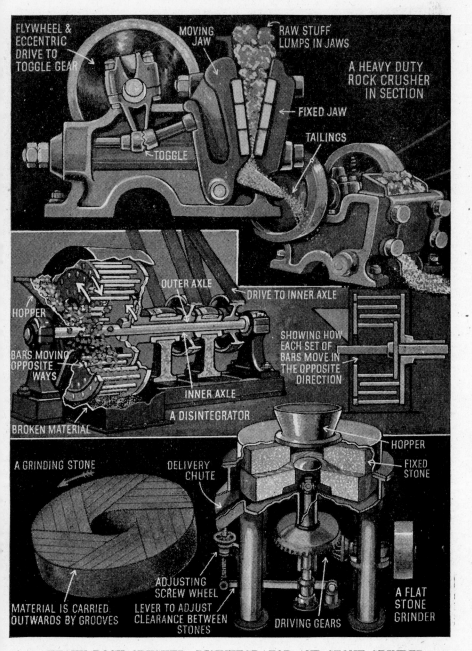

FLYWHEEL &
ECCENTRIC
DRIVE TO
TOGGLE GEAR

MOVING
JAW

RAW STUFF
LUMPS IN JAWS

A HEAVY DUTY
ROCK CRUSHER
IN SECTION

FIXED JAW

TAILINGS

TOGGLE

OUTER AXLE

DRIVE TO INNER AXLE

HOPPER

SHOWING HOW
EACH SET OF
BARS MOVE IN
THE OPPOSITE
DIRECTION

BARS MOVING
OPPOSITE
WAYS

INNER AXLE

A DISINTEGRATOR

BROKEN MATERIAL

HOPPER

A GRINDING STONE

DELIVERY
CHUTE

FIXED
STONE

MATERIAL IS CARRIED
OUTWARDS BY GROOVES

ADJUSTING
SCREW WHEEL
LEVER TO ADJUST
CLEARANCE BETWEEN
STONES

DRIVING GEARS

A FLAT
STONE
GRINDER

HEAVY ROCK CRUSHER, DISINTEGRATOR AND STONE GRINDER

Fig. 2. *The top part of the picture shows in section a heavy duty rock crusher of a very
powerful type. In the middle is a disintegrator, while in the lower part can be seen a stone
grinder very similar in principle to the ancient stone flour-grinding mill.*

effect the film is rather less durable than white lead, but it keeps its gloss better on exposure and, as the dirt in the atmosphere does not find such an easy surface on which to collect, the paint naturally retains its whiteness.

Lithopone is probably the most widely used white pigment for interior paints and enamels, but if possible it should be avoided for outside painting, as it tends to cause cracking of the paint film, and after a time washes off slowly with the rain—a process known in the trade as chalking. It is an extremely dense pigment, possessing greater obliteration or hiding power than white lead or zinc oxide, and is very suitable for the manufacture of undercoats and distempers. It is made by roasting zinc sulphide and barium sulphate together and is non-poisonous.

Antimony oxide is another white pigment used very largely in hardgloss paints, but as it has the effect of causing slow drying in paint films it is usually blended with other pigments to offset this feature. Furthermore, it is very expensive and this usually precludes its use when cost has to be considered.

Titanium oxide is the most opaque white pigment which exists, but as it sometimes causes rather bad "chalking" it is normally confined to paints for interior use or blended with other pigments for outside use where it is desired to improve their opacity.

BLACK PIGMENTS

There are many different types of black pigment available; probably the one most widely used is carbon black, which is produced in the U.S.A. by burning the gas from the oil wells and collecting the sooty deposit. It is extremely strong—that is to say, a very small percentage need be added to a white pigment such as lithopone in order to produce a comparatively dark grey.

There are many other types of black, such as lamp black (Fig. 6), mineral black, etc., which find a use in paints.

We next need to consider those coloured pigments which are made by a true chemical process, but before doing so must familiarize ourselves with a process known as precipitation (Fig. 7)—the method by which they are generally produced. If a solution of lead nitrate is added to a solution of sodium dichromate (both of which are water-soluble materials) a product which is insoluble in water will be formed and will settle to the bottom of the vessel. This is lead chromate as used in the trade, also called middle chrome.

PRECIPITATED PIGMENTS

These precipitated pigments divide into two groups:—(1) those which are made from chemicals of mineral origin, such as lead chromes in a range of shades from primrose to orange, Prussian blue, which is derived from iron compounds, and mixtures of lead chrome and Prussian blue which give us Brunswick greens: (2) those colours whose origin is organic and can be traced back to living matter, either vegetable or animal. In this class come all the very wide range of aniline dyes, which are precipitated in a form which is insoluble in water. Probably the one most familiar to us is monolite red, which is used on pillar boxes.

These dyes are today manufactured almost entirely from derivatives of coal tar and the older types from vegetable products; animal products such as cochineal are virtually obsolete.

In the dry colour works the solutions are made in tubs and run into large precipitating vats under very strict chemical control, the precipitated colours being allowed to settle and the top liquids run off. The pigment sludge has the bulk of its water removed

CHARGING AN EDGE ROLLER MILL

This takes its name from the grinding or rolling being done by a wheel on edge, here a stone one, seen behind the rails. Pigment is being shovelled into the mill for finer grinding.

mechanically in a filter press; the resulting cakes of pulp colour are dried in stoves, the temperature, which has an important effect upon the colours, being rigidly controlled. The materials are then powdered on mills such as edge runners to convert them into suitable products for the paint maker.

Having learned something of the pigment side of the business we can now turn to the liquid or vehicle.

In the ordinary type of ready mixed paint, such as one buys from a builders' merchant, the pigments are ground in an oil medium. The oil usually employed is linseed oil, made by crushing the seed of a flax plant which is grown in India and Argentina. After crushing, the oily mass is filtered and treated with acids and alkalis to form the refined varnish oil. This oil has the property of drying; that is, when a thin film of the

oil is spread over a surface the liquid slowly changes into a solid because of the absorption of oxygen into the film of oil. Normally the whole process takes a matter of three or four days, but the chemist has found that the addition of some metallic compounds help this absorption. Solutions of these compounds are called driers or terebenes.

It was found that when these oils are heated to a very high temperature they increase in viscosity or "thickness", and the resultant heat-treated oils are called stand oils or boiled oils. These oils dry much more quickly than the raw oil, giving better films and imparting better flow to the paint. The ready mixed paint is therefore usually pigment which has been ground in mixtures of stand oil and boiled oil.

These paints suffer from the fact that they are slow drying and have initially

E.T.T.S.—H*

fairly soft films. Let us see, then, what other types of medium or varnish are available.

The general definition of a varnish is a solution of a solid in a liquid. The most simple types are called spirit varnishes or lacquers. These are made by dissolving a gum in a suitable solvent, the method of manufacture being to place the gum together with the solvent in a rotating drum and then to churn it until all the gum has dissolved. In this way are made solutions of gum such as resin, manilla and shellac, in solvents such as methylated spirit or turpentine.

UNSUITABLE FOR EXTERIORS

All these types give varnishes which have excellent gloss and hardness, but because of the nature of the gum they are unsuitable for any exterior work either as varnishes or as paints. Their use is therefore limited to such things as decorative finishes for furniture, including the well-known french polishes.

The ancient Egyptian artists used resins in the form of soft sticky gums which were knifed on to the object and then allowed to cool and set hard. The amber colour of the resin was likened to the golden coloured hair of Queen Berenice and through the ages this has been altered from Berenice to verenice, then to vernix and varnish.

The main difficulty confronting the varnish maker was how to apply these hard durable resins in an easy manner. The natural gums are found in various countries as exudations from different types of trees, which are tapped by the natives. In other types the trees themselves give out a sticky mass which runs into the ground and over a period of years fossilizes into large lumps of very hard transparent resin. By far the most common and most useful of these gums are the copals obtained from Africa and Australia. These are exceptionally hard

resins of a very durable nature, but suffer from one serious defect—they are insoluble in oil. In order to make them oil-soluble the gum has to be "run", and the following method is employed by the varnish maker.

The gum is heated in an iron, copper or steel pot to temperatures ranging between 600° F. and 700° F. During the heating violent bubbling and frothing occurs, the gum breaks down and gives off very inflammable gases which have to be carried away from the pots in special flues. After a time the molten mass assumes a characteristic appearance and, at this point only, the gum becomes oil-soluble. At this critical stage the oil is added to the hot gum in small quantities at a time, making sure that the gum remains in solution. When all the oil has been added the varnish maker continues to heat the mass until he gets a stable mixture and one that he knows by experience will produce the correct film-forming characteristics. While this is still molten, driers are added in the form of the metallic oxides which combine with compounds in the varnish and improve the water resistance and weathering of the film. The "solids" of the varnish now being complete, it is necessary to add thinners such as turpentine, white spirit, naphtha, and so on, thus completing our solution.

CONVALESCENT PERIOD

This is the general procedure when making the natural gum varnishes such as the gold sizes, flatting varnishes and long oil mixing varnishes. When this is done, however, owing to the extreme temperatures used, the varnish is under great strain and has to undergo a "convalescent period" when it is stored in tanks to allow these strained conditions to settle down. After storage for definite periods the varnish is filtered and becomes a transparent golden liquid.

GRADING PIGMENT PARTICLES BY LEVIGATION

Fig. 3. *Ground under water in the edge runner (top left), the pigment is graded by its own settlement in a series of water tanks. The heavier particles sink more rapidly while the lighter and smaller pass on to the medium and finer tanks. Inset are shown two forms of edge runner, one which works in an open tray and the other for grinding under water.*

FILLING FROM AN EDGE GRINDING MILL.

The attendant in the foreground is filling tins with finely ground pigment from an edge-roller mill. The large stone roller can be seen in the tray above him.

We have seen that the need for tanking is due mainly to the excessive heat required to run the gum. Fortunately, of latter years the chemist has helped to improve the solubility of these natural gums by converting them into a more soluble form called esters. These require only moderate heat treatment to incorporate them with the oils; thus tanking for this type is eliminated.

Nearly all these natural resins have some disadvantage; for example, manilla and shellac have poor solubility in common solvents, resin has poor weather resistance and the copals require drastic heat treatment. The chemist, therefore, set to work to produce from pure chemicals a substance which would have all the advantages of the natural resins without their disadvantages.

These developments have given us the synthetic varnishes or media; these can be classified into two large main groups, although there are many others.

The phenolin resins are obtained by heating one of the family of chemicals known as the phenols, such as carbolic acid, together with formaldehyde. The reaction is very vigorous and much supervision is needed; at one stage the resultant product is a tough hard resin which can be made into varnishes on heating with different classes of oils. These varnishes give a much higher resistance to water than do the natural varnishes and, therefore, help greatly in the durability of the paint. Another class of synthetic resins called alkyds are made from such chemicals as phthalic acid, glycerine and certain

LEAD GRILLS

THE CAST
LEAD GRILL USED
IN THIS PROCESS

TIMBER FLOORING

POTS HALF FILLED WITH VINEGAR

SPENT OAK BARK TAN →

THE GRILL
AFTER CORROSION

TAN: GIVING OFF CARBON DIOXIDE FUMES

LEAD STRAPS
HUNG OVER BARS

VENTS FOR
CORRODING FUMES

STONEWARE PIPES DELIVERING STEAM,
CARBON DIOXIDE & ACETIC ACID FUMES

TWO METHODS OF MAKING WHITE LEAD

Fig. 4. *White lead, one of the most important materials used in the manufacture of paint, is made from ordinary lead by means of corrosion. Two alternative methods for its production are here shown; above, the stack process; below, the chamber process.*

derivatives of the oils. These materials react together; they can be controlled easily and manipulated to give a wide range of varnishes suitable for every need. They also possess the outstanding feature of giving paints of quick drying natures with exceptional durability.

We now can see that there is a variety of media to choose from for the manufacture of everyday enamels and undercoats. When producing undercoats it is usually desirable to make a paint which dries flat, and this can be achieved by using a high percentage of pigment and volatile thinners in relation to the non-volatile part of the medium, which would be linseed oil, gum, etc. Naturally, the thinners will evaporate, leaving behind the pigment with insufficient non-volatile liquid to dry with a gloss.

To cover the very wide range of paints used in modern industry is beyond the scope of this article. We should, however, note that stoving processes are used very largely nowadays owing to the speed of production which they make possible. In one hour at 250° F. an enamel can be made to dry to a degree of hardness which would be quite impossible to reproduce by air-drying methods. The formulation of stoving enamels requires a distinct technique, but it can be said that the medium employed is usually one containing a fairly high percentage of gum in relation to the oil.

Let us here consider that separate class of lacquers and enamels known as cellulose. In the search for new materials a substance called cellulose nitrate was

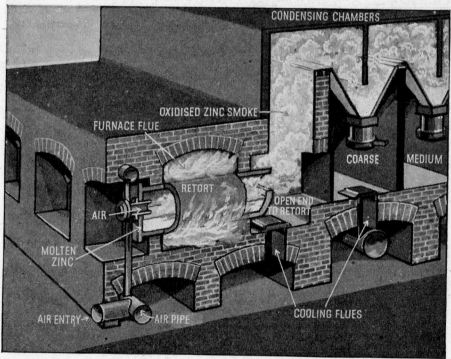

HOW ZINC OXIDE IS MADE

Fig. 5. *Zinc is first of all melted by heat and the fumes are mixed with air. This oxidized zinc smoke then passes to condensing chambers, where it is cooled and turned to powder.*

BATTERY OF HIGH PRESSURE GRINDING MILLS

High-pressure enamel grinding mills as here seen have speeded up production by reducing the number of grindings which are required in order to obtain a given degree of fineness.

made by treating materials like cotton linters with nitric acid. The resultant material, which has the appearance of a white, fluffy solid, was found to dissolve readily in special types of thinners, forming thick, colourless syrups which, owing to the nature of the solvents used, dried in the matter of a few minutes. The main objection to this type of finish is the extreme inflammability of both the solvents and the cellulose nitrate itself. Since then another material, cellulose acetate, has partly replaced the nitrate because it is non-inflammable, but here again the solvents are highly inflammable.

As these solutions dry by evaporation in a very short space of time, cellulose enamels were used for the quick finishing of mass-produced articles such as motor cars. The English motor car may have as many as 5 to 8 coats of cellulose sprayed on it before it is really finished, and this is possible only because in about a quarter of an hour the solvents have evaporated, leaving a dry film that can be re-sprayed.

Another advantage of cellulose materials is the very easy way in which the paints can be adjusted. Gum can be added in solution to improve the hardness and gloss of the product, or softening agents called plasticisers can be introduced to make it more pliable.

To proceed with methods of paint manufacture, that is to say, the process of incorporating the various types of pigment and liquids: we shall assume that our formulation has been decided upon and refer first of all to the production of an ordinary oil paint which can be mixed and sold ready for use.

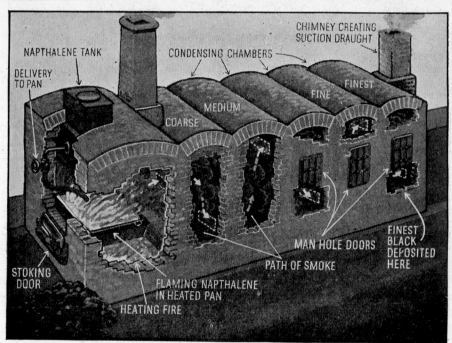

MAKING BLACK PAINT FROM SOOT

Fig. 6. *Lamp-black is produced from the smoke of burning naphthalene, condensed in a series of chimneys, where the soot is deposited in varying degrees of fineness.*

PRODUCING CHEMICAL PIGMENTS BY PRECIPITATION

Fig. 7. Chemical pigments are usually produced by the simple method shown above. The chemicals, mixed as fluids, produce a solid which sinks to the bottom of the vat.

In past days the decorator was in the habit of merely mixing together his dry pigment and liquids in the paint pot, so making his own paint. A product thus made, however, is far from satisfactory, as it is very coarse in texture and lacks good finish and covering power. The procedure in the paint works is to mix the pigment with a proportion of the liquid in a pug mill, then grind the resulting paste through some form of grinding mill. This may be one of many kinds. One kind is a triple roller mill in which three granite or steel rollers revolve at varying speeds in opposite directions, the middle roller revolving with a lateral motion which gives additional friction between the rollers.

Another type of machine is the flat stone mill, a development of the mill which was at one time used largely for flour grinding, with a water cooling arrangement to prevent excessive loss by evaporation and discoloration of the pigment due to overheating. After the

paste is ground it is run into a thinning tank where the remaining liquid is added and adjustments to colour, etc., are made; it is then filled into the tins.

In modern works these processes are sometimes carried out on different floors; this results in "gravity flow", which avoids excessive handling.

With the manufacture of hardgloss paints the operation is similar, except that far more attention has to be paid to the degree of grinding. An extremely fine product is needed if we are to obtain a film whose gloss will be free from little coarse particles—referred to in the industry as "seed". To obtain this fine grinding the product needs often to go through the mill two or more times, although in recent years certain high pressure mills have been placed at the service of the manufacturer, and have tended to speed up output.

When hardgloss paints are ready to be filled, some manufacturers pass the material through a centrifugal machine

GUM RUNNING OR MELTING SOLID RESIN

Hard, durable resin becomes soluble only at high temperatures. In these drums it is being melted and stirred, after which the oil will be added to form varnish.

to remove any slightly coarse material which may have found its way through the mill. These machines are somewhat similar to the separator which is used for removing the cream from cows' milk.

We ought not to leave paint manufacture without some reference to water paints or distempers. The commonest form is ordinary whitewash, which the decorator can make by adding whiting to glue size. This, of course, has many disadvantages, the chief one being that it rubs off; but the paint makers realised that if some way could be found of introducing a drying oil such as linseed oil into whitewash, a washable film could be produced.

This idea led to the manufacture of the many brands of washable distempers now on the market. The only important point is that the pigment, instead of being composed of whiting, often contains a large percentage of a more opaque material such as lithopone, in order to improve the hiding power.

The process of distemper-making is fundamentally fairly simple; it frequently consists merely of grinding the pigments in an edge runner with a liquid, which may be a linseed oil emulsion. The better grades are sometimes passed through a triple roller mill.

In the space available it has been possible to touch only very briefly on an industry whose importance is not always realised. Because of their power of protecting metals and other substances from the destructive effects of wind and rain, paints and varnishes have a valuable part to play in industry; for domestic use, indeed, it is doubtful whether they will ever be superseded.

GRAMOPHONE RECORDS

Sound Waves and How They Travel. The Diaphragm. Edison's Talking Machine. Disk Records. Recording Room. Master and Mother. Record Material and its Manufacture. Modern Methods. Microphone and Pick-up.

In 1877 Leon Scott caused a sheep-skin diaphragm, with a bristle stuck on it, to make a record track on a smoked card, purporting to show the vibrations set up by various sounds. Whether he realised the possibilities of his work we do not know, for his name passes out and is heard no more. It is to the famous Thomas A. Edison that we have to turn for the development of the talking machine, as the gramophone was originally called.

Before going any further, it will be as well to fix in our minds the nature of what we call sound. According to the dictionary, the word denotes both the sensation we receive through the ear and the external disturbance that causes this sensation. Now, all kinds of things produce sounds, but perhaps one of the simplest is the twanged stretched string or wire of a musical instrument.

SOUND FROM VIBRATION

Vibrating back and forth at a speed varying with its length and the degree of stretch, it sets up a musical sound, of high pitch for a short wire, low for a long one. There is no noise in the wire itself: it is the fact that each whip or vibration alternately slaps the air and releases it, setting up waves of high pressure and low pressure—called rarefaction by the scientist. These waves travel outwards, spreading in all directions, and, of course, weakening as they spread. But there must be a medium to carry them, for without air, or some other gas or substance, even solid, through which the waves can be transmitted,

no sound can either be set up or travel.

Unless some arrangement is provided to record these waves, there is still no such thing as sound. Fortunately nature has endowed each one of us with that marvellous sound-recording apparatus, the ear, the nature of which is not fully understood even to-day.

Picture a thin, tough skin stretched across a round hole; let us call it a diaphragm. Sound waves impinging upon it cause it to vibrate to and fro in time with the source of sound, and to continue doing so as long as it is affected by those waves.

The shaking diaphragm gives us

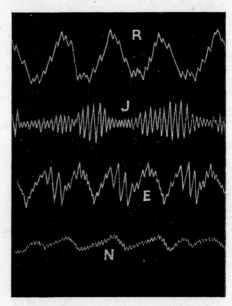

EVERYDAY SOUND WAVES

Fig. 1. *Some examples of the waves produced when we pronounce certain letters.*

another method of producing sound; we find that, if it can be vibrated rapidly enough, sounds are set up, its surface slaps the air in contact with it just as the twanging wire did and the waves move in the same way. If we make our diaphragm out of a sheet of very thin iron and put an electro-magnet behind it, we are well on the way to making not only a talking but also a listening machine (see Fig. 7).

Now the note, or noise, resulting from any set of waves is entirely dependent for its pitch upon the number of the waves set up in any given time. If we want to produce a note equivalent to middle C on the piano, then the string must shake 261 times a second, setting up a train of waves which travel outwards at 1,140 feet a second. From this it is evident that each wave will be a little more than four feet long. More rapid vibration than this produces a higher note; slower vibration produces a lower note. Generally speaking, the human ear can deal with vibrations from 16 up to about 38,000 per second as its absolute limits; some animals, dogs for example, can hear higher sounds, produced by more frequent vibrations, inaudible to the human ear. The B.B.C. broadcasts only between limits of 50 and

8,000, and not many loudspeakers can handle even this. Most of us can get along very well—as far as speech and music are concerned—between limits of 50 and 5,000. The purport of all this will be made plain in a moment.

Just as the human ear uses a stretched skin to record these waves, so can some kind of vibrant material such as a thin iron sheet, or that queer transparent mineral mica, be fixed in a frame and made to vibrate under their impact. If a light point is fixed to the centre with wax a record can be made of these vibrations, which at best are very tiny.

Edison figured out that such a record could be made on a soft metal drum, rotated at a steady speed and carried along, as by a screw, at the same time, so that a spiral track would be marked out by the slight indentations made by the point. He therefore had a machine made to provide this movement (Fig. 2), covering the drum with a sheet of smooth tinfoil. When the time arrived for the trial, naturally the inventor's voice was the one to be recorded, so Edison recited into the mouthpiece:

"Mary had a little lamb,
  Whose fleece was white as snow:
  And everywhere that Mary went
  That lamb was sure to go."

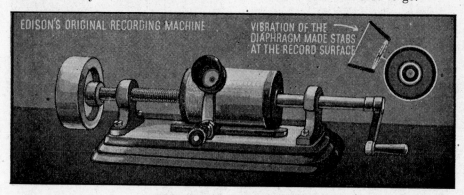

EDISON TALKING MACHINE

Fig. 2. *Compare this primitive machine, with its crude cylindrical records, with the modern disk record gramophone with its extreme accuracy of reproduction.*

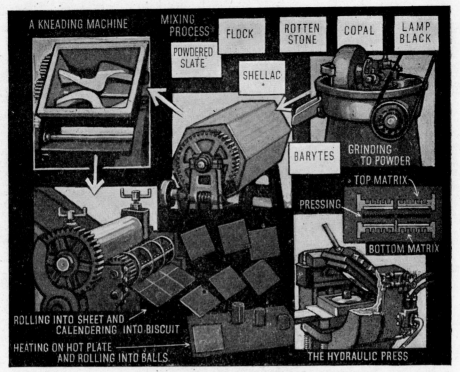

A KNEADING MACHINE | MIXING PROCESS | FLOCK | ROTTEN STONE | COPAL | LAMP BLACK | POWDERED SLATE | SHELLAC | BARYTES | GRINDING TO POWDER | TOP MATRIX | PRESSING | BOTTOM MATRIX | ROLLING INTO SHEET AND CALENDERING INTO BISCUIT | HEATING ON HOT PLATE AND ROLLING INTO BALLS | THE HYDRAULIC PRESS

MAKING RECORD MATERIALS

Fig. 3. *Processes involved in making the wax from which records are produced. A mixture formed from the materials indicated is first crushed to a high degree of fineness, then rolled again and again between steam-heated rollers.*

So was one of man's most remarkable devices launched forth on the world. A separate diaphragm for playing back had been provided; when this was adjusted into the indented groove of the foil and the handle turned, the unmistakable voice of Edison was heard, albeit blurred and indistinct.

So was the human voice first recorded, though the *transmission* of speech sounds had taken place before this; it was, indeed, Edison's experiments with the newly-invented telephone that had led him to make this trial.

Two schools of thought now emerged. One kept to the original idea of making the record on a cylinder, but the other school worked on the disk idea. This latter is the only one with which we need concern ourselves, for it soon held the field entirely in musical reproduction. Cylinders are today used only for office dictating machines. They are not permanent and are very difficult to reproduce—one reason why the cylinder went out of favour.

It is not necessary for the record to be limited to an indented line; a much better scheme is to engrave a wavy track, which will be continuous and smooth, so making for the elimination of unwanted noises. A perfectly clear note—which is very difficult to produce—would be represented by a single wavy line, disposed equally on either side of a central zero line, indicating no

BAKING THE BISCUIT

Fig. 4. *The square of wax is baked to a plastic condition ready to be placed on the die to make a record.*

circular. So long as the track is true, no vibrations will be passed to the diaphragm, and no sound will be emitted. But if the track is given a wavy form similar to that shown in the diagram (Fig. 1), then sound will be the result. It is not, of course, possible to put a deeply waved line on the record such as the one used to illustrate the principle, but it is the character of the wave that counts.

Taking an eight-inch record as an example to begin with, we may find that the space covered by the track spiral is about $2\frac{1}{2}$ inches wide, and into that space are crowded about 220 lines. This means that the total width of space for each groove, including whatever degree of wave is imposed on it, must not much exceed one hundredth of an inch. It will need very detailed study with a strong glass in a bright light before you can distinguish any very definite characteristics such as those described. And yet they are there; in the record under consideration there is a continuous needle track nearly 2,000 inches long, and every inch is made up of these wave forms. The illustration in Fig. 1 shows one or two examples of the kind of wave form associated with the pronunciation of certain letter sounds by the human voice. The first records were made by direct vibrations of the cutting needle from the voice or the instruments performing. The recording room was a bare, cheerless chamber with a trumpet cone projecting from one wall, and into this the performance had to be directed when a light signal was given. As a rule several performances were required

motion at all. If the sound is falling off in intensity, the wave crests decline in height until they flatten out to the zero line. So long as the wave *length* remains constant, so does the intensity of the note or sound produced.

It has been found that the twanged string, or for that matter any musical instrument, emits one principal vibration representing the true note it is adjusted to play, but in addition other vibrations are also set up having different frequencies. These are called overtones, and it is their existence which makes it possible for the listener to distinguish between one musical instrument and another. Anyone can tell the difference between the human voice, a flute, a piano, and a violin, even if they are all producing the same note. The reason for this is their overtones.

The grooved track on the gramophone record is, of course, continuously curved, and may be considered perfectly

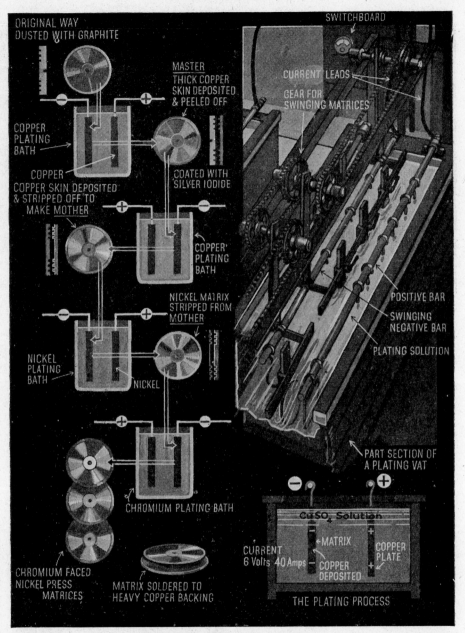

ORIGINAL WAY
DUSTED WITH GRAPHITE

MASTER
THICK COPPER
SKIN DEPOSITED
& PEELED OFF

COPPER
PLATING
BATH

COPPER
COPPER SKIN DEPOSITED
& STRIPPED OFF TO
MAKE MOTHER

COATED WITH
SILVER IODIDE

COPPER
PLATING
BATH

NICKEL MATRIX
STRIPPED FROM
MOTHER

NICKEL
PLATING
BATH

NICKEL

CHROMIUM PLATING BATH

CHROMIUM FACED
NICKEL PRESS
MATRICES

MATRIX SOLDERED TO
HEAVY COPPER BACKING

SWITCHBOARD

CURRENT LEADS

GEAR FOR
SWINGING MATRICES

POSITIVE BAR

SWINGING
NEGATIVE BAR

PLATING SOLUTION

PART SECTION OF
A PLATING VAT

CuSO₄ Solution

MATRIX

COPPER
PLATE

COPPER
DEPOSITED

CURRENT
6 Volts 40 Amps

THE PLATING PROCESS

MAKING A "MOTHER" RECORD

Fig. 5. *When the recording has been cut into the wax, this is dusted with graphite and coated with copper by electrolysis. The resultant copper disk, known as the "master," is then peeled off and further coated with nickel to protect it, and by further immersion the "mother" is made from which the records as actually used will be pressed.*

THE RECORD IS PRESSED

Fig. 6. *When the baked wax is soft it is put on the die and pressed into a record.*

before a satisfactory result was achieved. The difficulty of getting an adequate effect from a large orchestra can be imagined.

To the recording end of the process we shall return later. We turn now to the mechanical side of the work, as it appears on the other side of the wall at the small end of the trumpet. This part of the process has changed but little since the early days. We have a simple machine (Fig. 8), consisting of a turntable revolved at a constant speed by a falling weight, a method still in favour in spite of competing arrangements which have been claimed as improvements. The trumpet connects up with the diaphragm to which the cutting jewel—a tiny point of sapphire—is attached, and a screw thread carries this across the surface of the turntable, the threaded spindle being driven by gears from the turntable axis. The recording is made on the surface of a disk about

an inch thick made of a waxy composition that varies somewhat in different circumstances, its colour ranging from pale yellow to dark brown. A little guide wheel supports the cutting point to keep it at a constant depth and prevent any digging.

Once the recording engineer is satisfied with the job, the wax is dusted off to clear it of all sign of shavings, and is then thoroughly impregnated with graphite in the finest possible powder form to make it electrically conductive. This done, the excess graphite is carefully removed by a swiftly spinning brush, and the whole transferred to the electro-plating bath.

Here it will be hung on to the negative busbar, immersed in a bath of copper sulphate solution, facing a plate of pure copper hung from the positive bar. When current is turned on, a film of pure copper begins to deposit on the graphited face of the wax, and this film

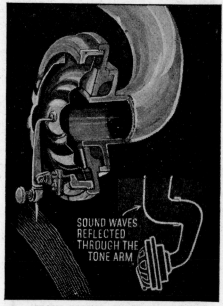

SOUND WAVES REFLECTED THROUGH THE TONE ARM

HOW SOUND IS TRANSMITTED

Fig. 7. *How the sounds made by vibrating the diaphragm are translated into grooves.*

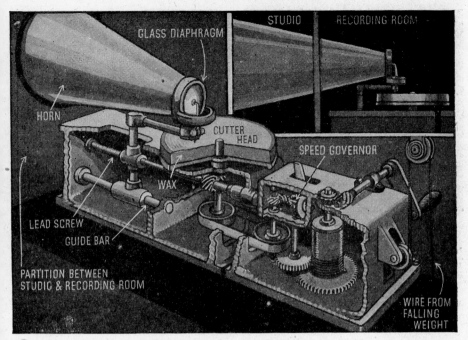

FROM STUDIO TO RECORDING ROOM

Fig. 8. *The method by which sounds received by the trumpet are first recorded on to the wax. The cutting jewel travels round a turntable revolved by a falling weight.*

grows in thickness as time goes on, a period of about 36 hours being usual. All the time the solution is kept stirred.

When the thickness of this skin of copper is judged sufficient, the wax is removed from the plating bath, the skin is peeled off and flattened. The wax is, of course, exactly the reverse of the copper, in which the wave-track stands up above the surface instead of being cut into it as with the original. The copper disk is the "master", and several more will be made exactly like it, though not yet. The master must be further protected from damage, since copper is soft. It will go into another electro-plating bath, where its face will be covered with nickel. The whole process is shown in Fig. 5.

A "mother" record will then be made by putting this master back into the copper bath, having first coated the face with a special solution to prevent the new layer of copper from sticking to it. The result, of course, will be a grooved disk, exactly similar to the original wax.

Once more we have to reverse the face of the copy, for not yet can records be made. A number of nickel copies will be produced by putting the mother disk into the nickel-plating bath, and these copies, when backed on to heavy copper disks, serve as the dies for pressing out the actual records sold to the public.

The master record is carefully preserved, and any further dies for pressing will be made from the mother record only. There will thus be several references to the original always available.

Making the actual disk is a relatively simple affair, involving a hydraulic press. The various makers keep the

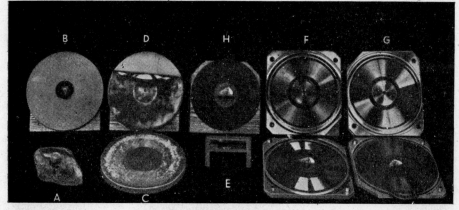

FROM RAW WAX TO RECORD

Fig. 9. (A) *Rough wax;* (B) *prepared for recording;* (C) *after recording;* (D) *copper master cut away to show original;* (E) *shellac used for recording;* (F) *matrices in mould plates ready for pressing;* (G) *record in mould plates after pressing;* (H) *finished record.*

composition of the material they use for the purpose more or less secret, but amongst those that are or have been used are various resins, shellac, barytes, rotten stone, flock from rags, and lampblack. The mixture is crushed to a great degree of fineness, mixed thoroughly and then rolled again and again between steam-heated rollers. The heat gives it some degree of plasticity, which is increased by the rolling. At the end of this process the material is in the form of a continuous flat plate about a yard in width, and the last rolling impresses grooves along and across it, dividing it into squares 12 inches wide (Fig. 3). It can when cold be broken into pieces of suitable size. The operatives refer to it, in this state, as "biscuit".

The hydraulic press can exert a pressure of 70 tons, and its ram and anvil accommodate a hinged die box that is made to withdraw for filling and so on. The bottom and lid of this box are hollow, and are connected to flexible pipes for a supply of hot steam or cold water, hot for pressing, cold for chilling after the press. A die is placed face upwards in the lower part of the box,

and on it, face down, the appropriate label. The same is done with the upper half. Now the operative bakes a biscuit (Fig. 4), heated to the plastic state, lays it in the box, closes the lid, the hot steam having been turned on, and it goes into the press (Fig. 6). Pressure goes on and the squeeze takes place. Next comes a pause for drilling, then the box is withdrawn and opened, when a brilliant new record appears in place of the dull square of biscuit that went in (Fig. 10). Its rough edges are swiftly trimmed off and polished. The stages through which the record goes are shown in Fig. 9.

While the making of records is not greatly changed since the early days, the recording process is now utterly different. With the advent of the modern microphone and its perfection, a new field opened up for the gramophone industry. It was now able to take in the performance of huge orchestras with the greatest of ease, and it became possible to take the recording studio to the performance, so that the recording could be carried out under ideal conditions. But more than that: the

PRESSING OUT A RECORD

Fig. 10. *When the nickel dies are ready for reproducing they are placed in a hinged die box in the hydraulic press. The biscuit of record material is then heated to a plastic state, rolled into a ball, and placed on the die over the label. The box is then closed and the ball pressed into a record under hot steam pressure. Above, an operative removing the record after pressing. It is now ready for the edges to be trimmed and polished. These presses exert a pressure of seventy tons.*

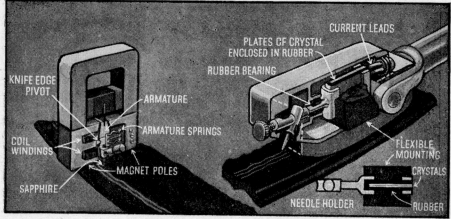

MODERN ELECTRICAL PICK-UP

Fig. 11. *In the radio-gramophone the sound box is replaced by an electro-magnet which sets up small vibrations. (Left) a magnetic cutter head used for cutting originals.*

vigorous electrical pulsations sent out by the valve-amplified pulses of the microphone could be applied to the record-cutting plant in a way that was virtually impossible when the performer had to drive that cutter himself, with only his breath to do it.

TYPES OF MICROPHONE

The microphones used are of various kinds. One in use by the B.B.C. is a ribbon microphone, in which a slender aluminium ribbon is fixed between the poles of a powerful electro-magnet. Sound waves impinging upon this ribbon cause it to flutter very slightly, but exactly in tune with them. This movement of an electrical conductor within the strong magnetic field sets up slight pulses of current in the magnet windings; these are noted and passed to an amplifier, where their strength is brought up to a degree sufficient for the cutter-head of the recording apparatus. Fig. 12 shows three types of microphone in use, ribbon, crystal, and condenser.

It is appropriate here to add a word or two about the actual playing of the record. Just as electrical recording has

made an enormous improvement in the quality of records, so has electrical playing improved the performance and life of the record. Almost everyone is acquainted with the mechanical reproducer, or sound-box. Its diaphragm is a disk of mica, or sometimes of aluminium, and connected to it by a spot of wax or other fastening is the stylus bar, pivoted at its lower end to a circular body into which the diaphragm is clamped between rubber gaskets. The body is carried on the end of the tone arm, into which it opens, and which is the small end of a long trumpet of scientifically expanded shape, doubled to and fro upon itself to save space. A needle socket is fixed to the end of the

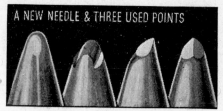

HOW THE NEEDLE WEARS

Showing the effect on the needle of the small movements in the record groove.

stylus bar, and the leverage of this bar multiplies the needle-point movement by two at least. Considering that the extent of the wave on the record cannot exceed at most about $\frac{1}{100}$ inch, this gives us a total to-and-fro motion of the diaphragm not exceeding $\frac{1}{50}$ inch.

The advent of the radio-gramophone brought a new delight to lovers of music. The so-called pick-up took the place of the old sound-box, and once this device had passed its teething stages it might be claimed that the best was being got out of the record. The pick-up is simply an adaptation of the principle that operates with the ribbon microphone; movement of an electrical conductor within the field of an electromagnet sets up slight currents of electricity in the magnet windings. One popular type has a thin, diamond-shaped piece of iron pivoted in rubber bearings, in between the magnet poles. The needle socket is fastened to the iron armature, and even the tiniest movements set up tiny currents that are amplified by the various valve stages in the radio set (Fig. 11).

The moving-coil type of loud speaker is probably capable of at least as good an output as the exponential horn of the average gramophone, good as the best designs are. But unless the quality is locked into those wavy grooves of the record, it cannot be reproduced by the best of instruments. The best records of today are absolute triumphs of manipulation of art and mechanical skill.

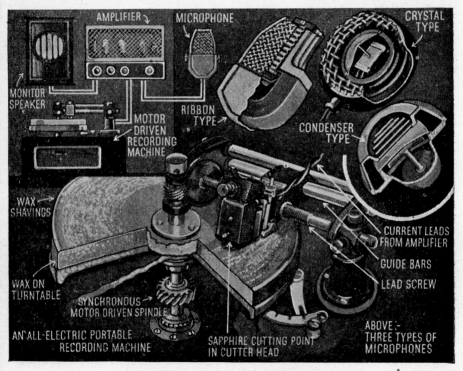

MODERN RECORDING METHODS

Fig. 12. *Three types of microphone used today. They represent a great advance from the days when the performer had to direct his recording straight into the trumpet.*

INDEX

ACKNOWLEDGMENTS

Thanks are due to the following for their courtesy in allowing use to be made of illustrations which are their copyright:—Lewis Berger *& Co., Ltd.; Bryant & May, Ltd.; B X Plastics, Ltd.; Carpet Trades, Ltd.; Courtaulds, Ltd.; De La Rue & Co., Ltd.; Ferranti, Ltd.; The General Electric Co., Ltd.; The Gramophone Co.,* Ltd.; The Imperial Tobacco Co.; Kodak, Ltd.; Pilkington Bros., Ltd.; The Postmaster General; The Royal Mint; The South Metropolitan Gas Co.; Stuart & Son, Ltd.; D. F. Tayler & Co., Ltd.; Wadkin, Ltd.; Josiah Wedgwood & Sons, Ltd.